Settled

Settled

How to Find Calm in a Stress-Inducing World

Chantal Donnelly, PT

New Degree Press

Settled

How to Find Calm in a Stress-Inducing World

ISBN 979-8-88926-814-7 *Hardcover*
979-8-88926-812-3 *Paperback*
979-8-88926-813-0 *Ebook*

For Aidan,

my best, most important reason for figuring out how to find calm.
I love you with all my heart.

Contents

Author's Note

Welcome! I'm so glad you're joining me.

Part 1 of this book will give you the foundational information needed to understand your stress.

Part 2 has the "settling tools." These are ways for you to regulate your nervous system so your stress responses don't feel so uncomfortable in your body. For easy reference, a consolidated list of these tools is outlined in the Settlement chapter at the conclusion of the book. There you will also find a scannable QR code with links to videos of the exercises.

Throughout this book, I share my story as well as the stories of other people. For privacy purposes, most of their names have been changed. Occasionally, the details of a story were modified to protect someone's identity or highlight a theme. A couple of stories are a combination of people's experiences, facts, or events. If I refer to someone using both their first and last name, you will know that I have permission to use their real identity.

This book is meant for informational purposes only and is not treatment for any medical conditions. It is not meant as a replacement for professional assistance. Please check with your physician before trying any of the movement exercises or tools included in this book. Please seek medical guidance, counseling, therapy, or a body-based practitioner should you need support.

Let's get started!

Introduction

I gave my patient Clara a gentle shoulder squeeze to signal that I'd finished mobilizing her spine. She sat up and swiveled around, her legs now dangling over the edge of the treatment table. Her hair was a little tousled—the aftereffect of my hands working on her neck. She smiled—the kind of peaceful, bright-eyed smile I knew well. It meant she felt better.

But as I walked over to my desk to book her next appointment, I hesitated. There was a heaviness to my movements. I wasn't burnt out, just frustrated. Something was lacking in my ability to fully help people. I felt there was a psychological component to Clara's—and others'—pain, but I didn't feel I had the tools to tackle it.

I had been a physical therapist for over twenty years. I loved my job. I was good at it. I had built a thriving private practice in Pasadena, California. My outpatient clinic was in a beautiful space with a modern aesthetic, high ceilings, two treatment rooms, and a Pilates studio. My patients were healing.

Yes. Clara *was* improving. Her debilitating headaches and neck pain were subsiding. But I knew the drill. She would feel better for a day or two, then the stress from her corporate job would trigger inflammation and knot up the connective tissues I had released during our session, then her pain would return. The same old pattern. I would unwind the tissue, and life would wind it back up again.

I had seen it with so many of my patients. If it wasn't a demanding job, it was a difficult relationship, or taking care of sick parents, or parenting sick kids, or facing financial hardships, or simply juggling a crushing schedule full of responsibilities.

Most people facing stress don't consider visiting a physical therapist ("physiotherapist" if you are in Canada or Europe). In general, our culture tries to solve stress-related problems with the mind, not the body. Humans are a brainy bunch. We extol the virtues of the intellect. We proudly cling to the notion that we can think our way out of any dilemma and the belief that we can do anything we "set our minds to."

But our responses to stress are physical—deeply rooted in ancient survival mechanisms. We forget (or we ignore, or we are unaware) that stress is a physical phenomenon. Our thoughts are powerful shapers of our realities, but it is our nervous systems that create our thoughts. Both the body *and* the brain need to be attended to if we're going to experience lasting relief.

That day, as Clara got off my treatment table, I decided to learn everything I could about stress. I wanted to help my patients more effectively, more completely. I felt elated that I had found the missing link: stress therapy.

At the time of this realization, I thought my career was heading for a complete makeover. But I soon discovered that physical therapy is the perfect complement to stress and resilience work. I can teach patients to mitigate pain by regulating their nervous systems, and my clinical experience and knowledge of the body bolster my ability to help people with their stress. It turns out that stress management through a physical therapy lens not only makes logical sense but adds an invaluable perspective: It meets stress where it lives.

Our society tends to pathologize being stressed-out. We think of it as a medical problem we need to cure. We believe that to be "better" people, we need to either control our stressors or stoically ignore our big emotions. Both goals—exiling all stress and being impervious to stress's effects—only lead to more unease. We internalize the message that if we are stressed out, we are weak, crazy, or inept. In this way, chasing calm becomes an additional source of stress.

It was for Clara. She had tried everything to decrease her stress: positive thinking, numbing, willpower, denial... When her body refused to play along with those strategies, she spent her earnings from her stress-inducing job trying to vacation, massage, and therapize away the discomfort.

There is a better way. The idea is not to force your stress into submission or oblivion (because that's impossible), but rather to understand your stress responses. These responses happen for biological reasons—not because of a character flaw or a lack of self-discipline. You don't need another time management class, more self-care, or to get up earlier and seize the day. Your stress responses are physical. They are natural, adaptive, and helpful. Calm isn't always the goal—because your stress responses can function as a guide, be useful motivators, or even enhance your ability to function.

You may be asking yourself, "If being stressed is so useful and biological, why am I reading a book about finding calm?" It's an excellent question (thanks for asking). Humans tend to get stuck in defensive stress responses, which, over time, erases the positive effects of stress and diminishes our abilities to listen to our bodies. We find ourselves overreacting to the small stuff, the big stuff, and everything in the middle.

A stress response to a taxing situation may be warranted; however, if that reaction is excessive in its duration or magnitude, it reduces our capacity to think logically, listen to our intuition, and make sound decisions. It zaps us of the energy we need to seek help or make changes. It also takes away our ability to distinguish between what's truly threatening and what is simply challenging us. And it can even make us sick.

Admittedly, my journey into the world of stress relief and resilience wasn't entirely for my patients. I, too, was wrestling with the demons of a pressurized world: pain, exhaustion, mood swings, despondency, emotional overload, and a critical mind. I felt stuck, and I was looking for answers for myself as well as for my patients.

In the past, I handled my stress by toggling between overcompensating and shutting down.

I had your typical type A, perfectionist personality. My time was used efficiently. My productivity was maximized. My achievements defined me. I controlled everything and everyone in my life. I chased adrenaline to fuel my forward progress. Control kept me tightly wound, but it also kept me from falling apart.

I got a college education, followed by a master's degree, became a mom, created and produced two rehabilitation videos, and blah, blah, blah. (I could rattle off my resume, or you could just read the "About the Author" section at the back of the book. You'll find a cute photo of me there as well.)

And then there were days when I couldn't (or maybe wouldn't) do it anymore.

As soon as I stopped pushing, I started feeling. I am not sure when it happened, but at some point during my thirties, I became allergic to stress. I don't mean stress made me sneeze (although there were times when lots of Kleenex was involved). It was not a histamine reaction; it was a hypersensitivity to stress.

The smallest amount of challenge or problem, and I broke. I either became reactive and irritable (usually starting arguments with the most cherished people in my life), or I shut down—too paralyzed to function. Yes. You are reading a book about stress from an author who was stuck and is a self-proclaimed "stress-sensitive" person. We teach what we ourselves need to learn (or so I've been told).

My ricocheting—from a driven, hypervigilant person who teeters between burnout and thriving to a stress-sensitive person who struggles to tolerate minor difficulties—is what compelled me to find middle ground.

That space between frantic and frozen is our destination together. There is a place of balance somewhere between using adrenaline-induced stress to propel you through life and being so "allergic" to stress that life's challenges become dead weight, dead ends, and, ultimately, soul-deadening. It is a place in the happy middle. A place I call the "Settled Section." A place where you can manage your stress instead of your stress managing you.

Perhaps my journey to the Settled Section resembles your path since the pandemic. Pre-pandemic lives tended to be overly-scheduled, high-anxiety affairs. The lockdown forced many of us to shut down. You might be moving to that middle point—trying desperately not to overshoot it and land back on the fast-moving treadmill of life.

Maybe your stress, like my client Tina's, feels like a burning sensation rising inside you like lava, and you're trying to stop yourself from exploding (or worse, imploding). You might be frustrated because all the things you have tried—meditation, exercise, psychotherapy, supplements, affirmations, self-care rituals—helped in the moment, but the fix was fleeting.

This book is about finding novel methods for managing stress and about approaching the old strategies differently, so that they do help us. We will spend a few chapters examining why we over-respond to stress or get stuck, and the remainder of the chapters looking at what we can do about it—the strategies that work.

This book is for anyone who is suffering because of stress and looking for relief. If you are a high-performing overachiever trying to avoid burnout so you can finally enjoy your successes, this book is for you. If you are sensitive to stress, and your sheltering strategies are keeping you from living life, this book is for you.

You will learn to understand your stress in a way that will stop the shame and denial often associated with feeling "stressed out." This new approach will widen your threshold for stress. It will improve your communication and connection with others (and with yourself). It will improve your health, enhance your creativity, and fuel your success.

If you are feeling the tug-or-war between drained and frenzied, you are in good company. This book will give you the framework and tools to nestle into neutral territory. Body-based tools for nervous system regulation were what I was missing for my patients and for my own wellbeing. Chances are, they can help you as well.

This book is a step-by-step guide on how to spend more time in the Settled Section. It will expand your definition of what is stressful and your definition of what is calming—and allow you to embrace both in equal measure.

CHAPTER 1

The Settled Section

Throughout my entire life, I have been on a stress rollercoaster. One minute I would be a frantic perfectionist: palms sweating, eyes darting, heart racing, thoughts ping-ponging everywhere, convinced the other people in the elevator were judging my shoes. The next minute I appeared as a confident, career-driven, exhausted soul with exceptionally organized closets. And just as often, I was a collapsed carcass of an individual: deflated, spent, unable to find the energy to drop off the dry cleaning or eat something beyond Doritos for dinner.

The transitions from one "stress extreme" to another often happened at warp speed. I could never find my footing to land in a place of moderation. The rapid ricocheting from one troubled way of being to the next gave me whiplash. No, for real; I'm not being poetic. I ended up with neck pain so severe that I chose a career in healthcare to try to heal myself.

Perhaps you too have something in life making you miserable—some event or situation driving you to your own personal brink. You may be thinking, "Other people have it worse than me; why am I such a basket case?" Or maybe you're really good at pretending everything is fine, but your insomnia, back pain, digestive issues, mood swings, or fragile immune system are daily reminders that everything is definitely *not* swell. Let me say this—and it's important: Nothing is wrong with you. Your stress is normal. Your feelings of being overwhelmed are not a reflection of your personal strength or your intelligence or your morals. Neither is that pint of ice cream you consumed last night. Stress is actually a biological phenomenon trying to help you.

The Stress Paradox

Our society has a paradoxical relationship with stress: We simultaneously encourage it and pathologize it.

We are urged to push ourselves—whether it's toward entrepreneurship, a flawless body, an Ivy League education, a second home, or whatever Mount Everest we're trying to climb. Google "comfort zone," and you'll be inundated with books, TED Talks, YouTube videos, podcasts, and articles like "The Power of Discomfort," "Life Happens Outside the Comfort Zone," and "Top-Five Electric Heaters" (okay, so it's also a portable radiator). But clearly (except when it comes to heaters), moving away from the "comfortable" and into the "uncomfortable" is seen as the magic fairy dust of personal growth.

However, showing signs of *being* uncomfortable is unacceptable. Pushing ourselves out of our comfort zones means pushing ourselves into a state of stress, yet our society treats reactions to stress—like anger, hopelessness, or anxiety—as "negative" emotions and personal failings. Detached aloofness and rugged grit get glorified, while any sign of being ruffled is met with a derogatory "Don't stress out!"

In our world of jammed freeways, packed schedules, and twenty-four-hour news cycles, it seems strange to treat being stressed as abnormal. It leaves us grappling with this contradictory societal message: Embrace the cult of uncomfortableness (in a world that's already horribly uncomfortable) while still seeming calm, cool, and collected.

But if we're *already frazzled* before taking this uncomfortable path to self-evolution, *how can we distinguish between the stress we're trying to embrace and the stress already suffocating us*? Once you've surpassed your stress threshold, the discomfort all feels the same.

The "push into uncomfortable" mantra is about *choosing* our stress—asking for a raise, starting a business, or swiping right on a dating app—in exchange for a shot at a better life (or so we are promised). But not all stress comes by choice. Stress can also land in our laps with a thud, unwanted and without purpose. A car accident, a layoff, a racist encounter, a scary medical diagnosis—these are just a few (of many!) unchosen discomforts.

Here's my issue with society's paradoxical attitude toward stress: We are encouraged to seek it out with no guidance on what to do with it. We are not taught *how* to get "uncomfortable" without hurting ourselves (and others). We're trying to push into the uncomfortable and just deal with the stress without a guidebook on how to proceed safely and effectively.

We need training on how to "do" stress—both the kind you choose by venturing out of your comfort zone *and* the kind that befalls you without your approval. We need a stress instruction manual.

This book is that manual.

Our Current Strategies

If our current stress-management techniques were helping, there'd be no need for a "how-to-stress" guidebook. But the prevailing methods don't seem to be working.

Trying to eliminate stress altogether is an exercise in futility. I'll share my attempts at this in a later chapter (News flash! It doesn't work.) Stress is inevitable, and trying to avoid it is stressful in itself. You end up missing opportunities, feeling frustrated, and *still* dealing with stress nonetheless.

Pushing Through Stress

A popular strategy is to push "through" the stress.

Toughness, grit, and persistence get a lot of praise, but from what I can see, they only fuel more stress. Hyper-driven and adrenalized, we play the Uncomfortable Game. Outwardly, we might even be playing it well—at least according to society's definition of success. Inwardly, however, things are not so hunky-dory.

Rates of burnout are sky-high. The go-getters embracing our hustle culture are beginning to buckle. Fixations on money, prestige, social media followers, and perfectly hacked bodies create accelerated, unstable lives, and the scurry to the top of the ladder fuels movies and memoirs about the lonely unhappiness at the upper rungs.

Numbing as Coping

Ways of momentarily numbing our stress are many: excessive eating, over-exercising, compulsive shopping, and overindulging in alcohol, gaming, gambling, pornography, or drugs. These help quell our anxieties in the moment, but they cause harm over time.

Avoidance, addiction, and hyper-driven living are perfectly understandable coping strategies given our tumultuous world. They protect us from being uncomfortable humans without a proper instruction manual. But these coping techniques are not sustainable—and, over time, they undermine our resilience.

Self-Care Conundrum

Some stress strategies seem healthy on the surface but are fraught with pitfalls. Self-care rituals like vacations, meditations, and "alone time" might momentarily extinguish the flames of stress, but somehow we still get burned.

We believe in the power of self-care because it allows us to "check out" for a while, often providing a much-needed respite from our stressors. But then we find ourselves snapping right back into high-stress survival mode as soon as we finish the yoga class or return from our walk or get back to real life after a long vacation.

Like the numbing techniques, the self-care strategies provide momentary escape from our stress, so we think they're working and we crave more. We become self-care junkies, living for the next run or spa treatment. The very strategy we use for soothing starts perpetuating our stress. If a work deadline keeps us from our bubble bath or golf game, we feel unglued—and further stressed. When the burden of self-care increases your stress, it is no longer self-care; it has become yet another stressor.

The need for more and more self-care is so strong because these methods are not really targeting our stress as we've been led to believe. They are diversions that do not get to the root of the problem. *Our downtime is not calming down our nervous systems.*

I'm not saying self-care doesn't work. Sometimes it does. But only if it squarely addresses the stress in your body. If it's only providing a stress interruption rather than a stress reduction, it's not truly taking care of you.

If you're actually regulating (or calming) your nervous system instead of just escaping, you have found the right de-stressing strategy for *you.* Teaching you how to know if your self-care is working for you is one of the goals of this book.

Positive Thinking

Another popular technique for dealing with stress is thinking positively. This philosophy suggests you can manipulate your experience of stress by changing your story about it.

Through cognitive reframing such as "look on the bright side" or "everything happens for a reason" we make ourselves feel bad about feeling bad. We shame and blame ourselves if we can't "buck up." Dismissing our misery with "it could be worse" only makes us feel worse.

Also, it's exhausting always being "on," pretending to be happy and acting like life's perfect, no matter how much is thrown at you. It takes a lot of energy to live like that. No wonder we see so much burnout and sickness among folks adept at pushing forward using optimism as a battering ram.

The broader problem with putting a positive spin on stress is that it takes a cognitive approach. When we're under a high level of stress, our brain is offline, and thinking our way through it isn't going to work. Trying to think our way out of stress is like trying to reason with a toddler having a tantrum. An upset three-year-old who's shaking, screaming, and flailing around on the ground is not going to hear your words—let alone understand them. When we're stressed, telling ourselves "everything is fine" and we "just need to calm down" misfires in much the same way.

Body-Up vs. Brain-Down

By thrashing about, agitated toddlers instinctively use body-based tools to calm themselves down. Adults need physical tools too; they just look a little different for us older folks. Our body-based techniques are more conscious and concise. (We will explore them in Part 2.)

When trying to find relief from stress, we tend to ignore our bodies. Our society prioritizes "brain-down" or "top-down" therapies. But feeling stressed is a body experience as well as a mind experience. In fact, an important part of your regulating nervous system—the vagus nerve (more on that in the next chapter)—has 80 percent of its fibers communicating from the body *up* to the brain and only 20 percent from the brain down to the body (Porges 2017, 33–34, 57).

This may explain why, for most people, a cognitive approach to stress isn't going to do much good until they get their body onboard. The body has a greater influence over the mind than the mind has over the body.

As I interviewed people for this book, I discovered a common pattern: They had all wrestled with stress, and traditional therapy had helped, but it wasn't until they started using somatic (body-based) tools that their healing jumped to the next level. Learning to address the body was the finishing touch for them. In time, it also helped their mindset or cognitive therapies to finally "stick."

Adults don't have the luxury of using the same flailing approach as toddlers, but there are body-up methods that work for us. Not as replacements for talk therapy or meditation (or whatever works for you) but as adjuncts. The body is often the key to unlocking an avalanche of self-expansion and relief. As well-versed as we are in the power of our thinking, *it is time to recognize and explore the power of our bodies on our thinking.*

No matter what path we take to relieve our stress, there continues to be a lot of hurt in our world. Some of us are shutting down, giving up, and being sucked into a downward spiral of shame and depression. Others are living a life of hypervigilance and frantic doing—a path often leading to exhaustion, dissatisfaction, emptiness, and a constant yearning for more. People are rarely able to settle somewhere in the middle of those two places. I certainly couldn't.

Pushing our way out of stress isn't working. *Self-caring* our way out of stress isn't working. And *thinking* our way out of stress isn't all that helpful either.

We need a different way.

There are simple things you can do to feel less wonky, and they don't involve harmful coping strategies, beating yourself up, or trying to control things that are out of your control.

When I started studying the nervous system, I learned to find the space between my stress extremes: the Settled Section. Turns out, it's where the brain-down and the body-up methods of managing stress meet up—somewhere around the heart.

When I'm in my Settled Section, I am sheltered from drastic vacillations in stress extremes; I am neither high-performing nor beaten-down, but rather steadfast and centered. I still get enraged, cry, grieve, or experience bliss here, but emotions don't overtake me. I am not devoured or knocked down by my feelings. We are able to co-exist. It's what professor of psychiatry Dan Siegel calls your "window of tolerance"—that place where you feel able to cope with stressors while retaining emotional stability, even during times of upheaval (Siegel 2020).

The tools I share in Part 2 helped me to expand my Settled Section—to widen my window of tolerance.

My life is better now. My relationships are stronger. My creativity isn't forced. My confidence is (mostly) more genuine. My self-care habits happen more naturally and with less need to numb or escape. Life unfolds and flows a lot more smoothly.

Don't get me wrong; I still experience stress—occasionally finding myself in a state of frenzied dismay or despondent immobility. Today, however, my relationship with stress is different. There's less of the violent back and forth. Less chance of whiplash. This is not a magic cure-all, but it is a way to spend less time at the sharp edges and more time nestled in the center.

I am not an expert on *your* stress. Only you can be that. But I have studied stress and the human body extensively, and I've managed to find some peace for myself. What I have learned from my deep dive into stress research—viewed through my physical therapist's lens—can help guide you on your own path to tranquility.

So, what are the step-by-step instructions that get us to the source of our stress? What will help us—not just to momentarily escape, numb, or put a positive spin on our stress, but to really address it head-on? Or should I say, to address it from the *body* up? Let's find out! Let the settling begin!

PART 1

Building the Foundation

Prior to discussing the details of finding your Settled Section and when and how to regulate your nervous system, we need to establish an understanding of what stress is and how we as humans respond to it.

Before we begin building our settle-ment, we need to pour the foundation.

Part One includes five key points in our step-by-step guide on how to stress:

Step One: Focus on Your Stress State and NOT on Your Stressors

Chapter 2 The Stress Quadrant

Step Two - Don't Try to Be Calm 24/7

Chapter 3 Calm Isn't Always the Goal

Step Three - Understand the Factors Influencing Your Stress State

Step One:

Focus on Your Stress State and NOT on Your Stressors

CHAPTER 2

The Stress Quadrant

When I lead workshops on stress and resilience, I start by asking this question: *How* do you know when you're stressed?

People will automatically rattle off their stressors: job insecurity, an argument, a demanding teacher, their daily commute, a loved one's illness, etc. Their natural inclination is to summarize their *stressors*, but what I am asking about are their *stress responses.*

Stress vs. Stressors

The term "stress" originated in the field of physics to describe pressure or tension on an object. When psychologists adopted it, they began using the word to mean "a state of mental or emotional strain or tension resulting from adverse or very demanding circumstances" (Oxford 2023).

In the early days, stress management focused on controlling and preventing stressors—the "adverse or very demanding circumstances."

In 1967, psychologists Holmes and Rahe created a stress scale ranking forty-three common events according to their degree of strain on an individual.

The death of a spouse was at the top of the list, earning one hundred points, while marriage landed squarely in the middle with fifty points, and a minor violation of the law (remember that speeding ticket?) was at the bottom with a value of eleven points (Holmes and Rahe 1967).

Typically, we *still* think of stress as an external force working against us. But "stress"—as a verb, not a noun—is an *internal* process. It's a brain-and-body experience, both cognitive and biological.

When people talk about stress, they are generally talking about *stressors*. Instead, I think we should change the discourse and make sure we're all talking about stress *responses.*

Stressors trigger our stress responses. These stressors can be monumental events or everyday annoyances. Size doesn't matter. The compounding of life's tiny pressures—sometimes referred to as "stress stacking"—can become harder to manage than the mammoth challenges. A taxed nervous system, like a weakened bone, becomes susceptible to stress fractures from repeated trauma.

Stressors are largely out of our control (remember that global pandemic?). Stress *responses*, however, give us a way to understand, leverage, and quell our uneasiness.

Stress responses are not universal. They vary from person to person. We now recognize that life circumstances don't carry universal units of stress as the Holmes and Rahe scale suggests. Each person responds to a new marriage or a new speeding ticket in a different way. *Stressors* are not as informative as the stress *responses* they evoke.

Some people seem "allergic" to stress (as I often am); others seem to thrive on it. One person's apathy towards a fender bender is another person's panic attack. There is no right or wrong response. These are biological, involuntary reactions.

Furthermore, our responses fluctuate from moment to moment. The same problem can be exasperating one day and innocuous the next. Sometimes, when I look at my teenage son's bedroom, smoke comes out of my ears! Other times, I just walk on by with a playful shrug.

Why Focus on Stress Responses?

Life's external stressors offer too much variability (between individuals *and* within individuals) to hold the answers we seek. So we will delve into the study not of stressors but of stress responses—because our internal reactions to these largely uncontrollable circumstances are the key to some relief.

Instead of asking, "*Why* am I so stressed out?" we can ask, "*What* is my stress response telling me?" This alters our relationship to stress. It brings our stress awareness to our bodies—to their biology and physiology.

People often think they'll only feel better once a stressor is gone, resolved, or ceased.

In reality, addressing our bodies' stress responses and learning to settle our nervous systems (even just a little) makes life less chaotic. We take in a wider view—assessing whether our response is helping us—and find we have more mental focus, physical stamina, social skills, and creativity to deal with our problems.

Suddenly, we can grab the steering wheel and change course with self-compassion. We have more bandwidth to take the necessary next steps—whether it's leaving a hurtful relationship, asking for a raise, seeking assistance, fighting injustice, or having that long-overdue conversation.

So, what exactly is a stress response?

Nervous System 101

Your reaction to stress originates from a part of your body that evolved over many millennia, your autonomic nervous system or ANS (warning: high school biology flashback!). This ancient part of your nervous system has two main branches: the parasympathetic nervous system and the sympathetic nervous system.

If you are dyslexic like me—or just not into science-y words—you might find it helpful to call the parasympathetic nervous system the "Stillness System" and the sympathetic nervous system the "Movement System."

The Stillness System is primarily made up of your vagus nerve. The word "vagus," which comes from the Latin word meaning "wandering" or "vagrant," is a cranial nerve that starts at your brainstem and follows a long and winding road (cue Beatles song!) to your lungs, heart, liver, kidneys, and intestines. Its many branches communicate with most of your organs, affecting their function via the release of a neurotransmitter (or chemical messenger) called acetylcholine, causing a decrease in heart rate and an increase in blood flow to the gut for digestion.

The Movement System is traditionally thought of as your fight-or-flight system. It originates within your spinal column, particularly in the middle area (your thoracic spine). This is your readiness system, which works in conjunction with the chemical messenger adrenaline. When our movement nervous system is at its peak, we feel frantic, anxious, irritable, and hurried. We're in a mobilized state, thinking in terms of "I should" and "I need to."

Our heart rate speeds up, our blood pressure increases, our muscles tighten, and our breathing becomes more rapid and shallow. We feel worried or angry, moody, restless, reactive, and impatient with ourselves and others. Time seems to move at an accelerated velocity, and we feel like we'll never have enough of it to get everything accomplished.

This state of high arousal and readiness makes it difficult for us to unwind and go to sleep. Not only is our physiology keeping us awake, but our mind's rapid, boomeranging thoughts are too. We get tunnel vision, often making us hyper-focused and distorting our ability to see the big picture.

I tend to speak with my hands, and when talking about the Movement System during my workshops, I'll put them up and flourish my fingers like a dancer in a production of *Cabaret*. I jokingly refer to the frenetic state of fight-or-flight as being universally represented by choreographer Bob Fosse's "jazz hands."

I once found myself in a high-stress situation where my instinctive (yet totally useless) response was "jazz hands."

It happened one late evening in August. My husband and I had just drifted off to sleep when a strange sound woke me up. I trudged over to the window and pulled open the curtains to find a man trying to break into my house! I screamed but froze in place. Except for my hands. My hands gave that burglar a good dose of jazz hands, and he ran away.

The Stress Quadrant

Stress shows up in the body in one of two ways: either you get more active, or you get more still (or, in the case of my burglar episode, both). Knowing which direction you're heading—speeding up or slowing down—helps you adjust the controls.

We think about stress and relaxation as being two distinct experiences, like a light switch that is either "on" or "off." But they actually work more like volume knobs or car brakes. You can have the volume somewhere between all the way up and all the way down. Similarly, you can have the brake partially depressed while the car is still moving.

In other words, these are spectrums, not all-or-nothing situations. The two parts of our ANS work together to give a more nuanced experience beyond just "calm" or "anxious." I created the Stress Quadrant to capture the gray areas and to show how the Stillness System and the Movement System work together.

For a helpful visual, let's plot the Stillness System on an x-axis and the Movement System on a y-axis. (As if the flashback to biology class weren't enough, I'm now taking you back to high school geometry.)

To remember which is which, imagine the horizontal line of the Stillness System (or x-axis) as a placid lake—a symbol of quiet stillness. Imagine the vertical line of the Movement System (or y-axis) as a fueled-up rocket—a symbol of pressure, tension, energy, and alertness. This y-axis is also a visual representation of your tall, upright spine where the sympathetic nervous system originates.

Now we have a horizontal x-axis representing our Stillness System and a vertical y-axis representing our Movement System. This forms a four-quadrant grid demonstrating how the two systems interact.

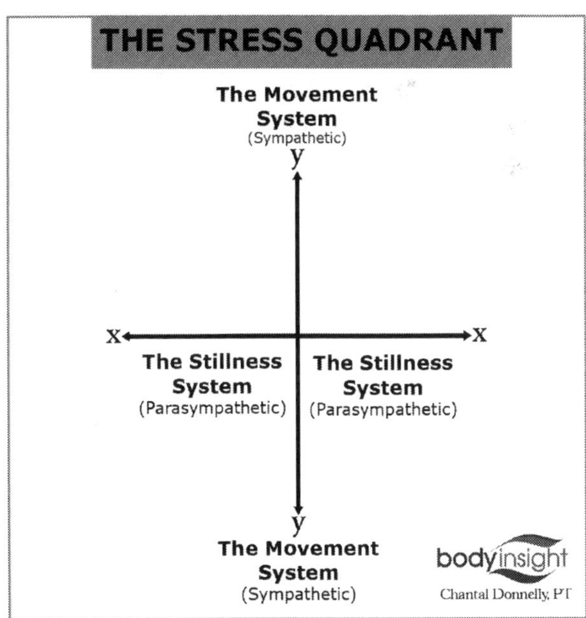

As you see from the graph, the Movement System and the Stillness System are each on a continuum. At the peak of the Movement System, you feel the tension and pressure associated with how we traditionally understand fight-or-flight. However, if you find yourself somewhere in the center of the Movement System—not too high and not too low (we will discuss the Goldilocks principle of stress soon)—you will experience a moderate amount of adrenaline and alertness that feels more like motivation, enthusiasm, productivity, and an energized drive. But what about the Stillness System? What happens as you move to the left or right of the x-axis?

Viva La Vagus!

Scientists knew the vagus nerve had two branches, but in 1994, behavioral neuroscientist Dr. Stephen W. Porges posited the two branches had different functions. His Polyvagal Theory ("poly" meaning "multi") stated one branch, the ventral vagal, was responsible for our Calm quadrant, and the other, the dorsal vagal, was responsible for Freeze (Porges 2017, 62).

Freeze

Going back to our grid, on the left end of that horizontal axis, we have Freeze. When the nervous system detects a threat it deems unmanageable, we land here. "Immobilized," "disconnected," "shut down," "collapsed," and "in dorsal" are other terms used for this stress response.

"Immobilized" is a good descriptor because, when we find harbor in this place, we don't feel motivated to move. We feel stuck, overwhelmed, hopeless, and contracted inward. With rounded shoulders and averted eyes, we disconnect from others and from ourselves. This is where we say, "I can't" and heavy emotions make us want to pull up the covers and disappear from the world.

The freeze response is a survival mechanism designed to protect us should we become trapped or injured and can't escape. Therefore, when we are in this quadrant, our bodies excrete natural opioids, which create an analgesic effect. This state makes us feel numb and clumsy and separate from our body. We may become forgetful, unfocused, and spacey. Our heart rate slows, and our eyes have trouble focusing. We might have a blank expression or a monotone voice. Our temporal sense becomes altered, so we feel as if time is dragging... by... painfully... slow.

I occasionally refer to this left side of the stillness continuum as "vampire stillness." It sucks the life force out of us. It is stillness without vibrancy, vitality, or sparkle. It's also an entirely appropriate and helpful stillness during times of extreme stress.

The Social Engagement System

The right side of the x-axis is more than just Calm. It is often called "safe and social."

Dr. Porges also found four *other* cranial nerves, besides the vagus, linked to the calming branch of the ventral vagal.

These four additional nerves (there's a chart at the end of the chapter) are responsible for helping us communicate with others—both verbally and non-verbally. They innervate the face and neck and allow us to speak, hear the human voice, and interact using facial expressions, head tilting, and shoulder shrugging. This will become critical information later because these four nerves are portals to accessing our vagus nerve and our calming nervous system.

I envision these four other cranial nerves like backup singers for the vagus and call their hit group "Vagus and The Quartet." These five cranial nerves working together are what Porges calls the "social engagement system" (Porges 2017, 6, 26–27, 134–140).

When we are in this system, we are relaxed and expansive. We feel connected to others and ourselves. This stillness has life, buoyancy, and vibrancy. We experience both positive and negative emotions in this state, but—unlike in the more defensive responses—the emotions do not overtake and define us. We have even breathing and moderate heart rates. Our faces and voices are expressive and our muscles are relaxed. In this state we feel safe and are curious, clear-headed, creative, focused, and at peace.

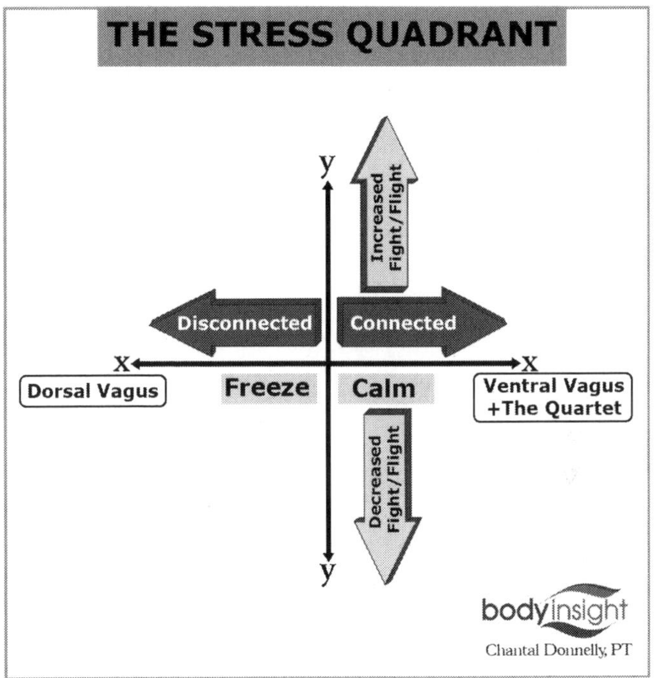

Re-defining Stress

So, the Stillness System has evolved to be responsible for both Calm and Freeze: both relaxation and a state of paralysis—*two very different responses*—surprisingly coming from the same anatomical structure. The one commonality between the two quadrants is they both involve a lack of movement, which is why I call this the "Stillness System."

At the beginning of this chapter, I gave you the dictionary definition of stress. But the Stress Quadrant uncovers a much more useful definition. According to the Stress Quadrant, stress can be defined as *an increase in arousal that has become overly uncomfortable or a stillness that has lost its vibrancy.*

As humans we spend our days toggling all over these four quadrants. Ideally, we bop around the matrix according to our situation. You read an upsetting email and are in high-activation on the Movement System for about an hour. Then you meet your friend and share a good laugh over lunch, and you move back to low-level Movement System mixed with a scoop of social engagement system.

The Stress Quadrant allows us to take in some of the nuanced states our ANS lands on. These "mixed states" are combinations of fight/flight and social engagement or fight/flight and freeze. You see mixed states in things like competitive sports, which combine social engagement (team interaction) and fight energy (aggression to play the game). My scary burglar episode is an example of freeze meeting fight/flight (note: I don't recommend "jazz hands" as an effective fight strategy).

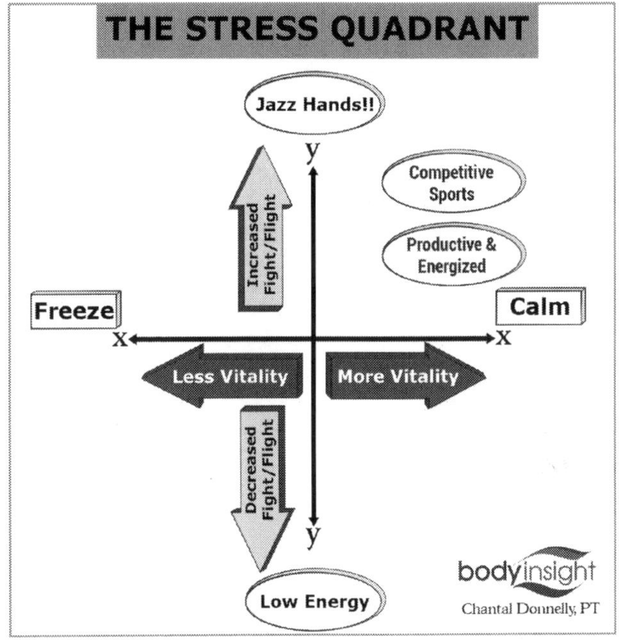

Sometimes we get stuck in an extreme region of the grid for a period of time. As I have mentioned before, I am working on spending most of my time in the middle. The Settled Section is a place where the Movement System energy is at a comfortable level and is mixed with some vibrancy from the social engagement system.

It is not always appropriate to be there, in the middle. At times, a more extreme stress response is warranted and we find ourselves in fight, flight, or freeze out of necessity. But being more centered within the continuum—being energized yet connected—is more realistic than always aiming for calm. In fact, calm isn't always the desired goal, as we will see in the next chapter.

All The Names of the Autonomic Nervous System (ANS)

STILLNESS SYSTEM

Parasympathetic Nervous System

Calm

- Rest and Digest
- Ventral Vagal
- Relaxed
- Social Engagement System
- Safe & Social

Freeze

- Dissociation
- Dorsal Vagal
- Immobilized
- Shut Down
- Collapsed

MOVEMENT SYSTEM

Sympathetic Nervous System

Fight or Flight
Fight or Flee
Mobilized
Arousal State
*Jazz Hands

▶ I am the only one who calls the Movement System "jazz hands" (just so you know).

▶ Both Freeze and Fight-or-Flight are referred to as "defensive states."

Chantal Donnelly

Cranial Nerves of the Social Engagement System

NO.	NAME	FUNCTION
V	Trigeminal	• Chewing • Biting • Sensations of the face
VII	Facial	• Facial Expressions • Some Taste • Some hearing
IX	Glossopharyngeal	• Taste • Speech • Social Vocalizing • Swallowing
X	Vagus	• Digestion • Breathing rate • Heart rate
XI	Accessory	• SCM and trapezius muscles • Head tilting and roataing • Shoulder shrugs/ body language

bodyinsight Chantal Donnelly

Physical, Mental, and Emotional Characteristics on the Stress Quadrant

SOCIAL ENGAGEMENT SYSTEM	FIGHT/FLIGHT	FREEZE
• Creative • Clear thinking • Flexible thinking • Positive outlook • Relaxed muscles • Expressive face • Expressive voice • Easy digestion • Patient • Interactive	• Over or under focused • Rigid thinking • Repetitive thinking • Negative outlook • Shallow, fast breathing • Constipation • Restless • Agitated • Shaky • Fast speech • Eyes darting • Poor sleep • Impatient • Self-focused • Confrontational	• Spacey (blank mind) • Scattered thinking • Hopeless • Very tight or flaccid muscles • Forgetful • Confused • Numb • Apathy • Flat facial expression • Monotone voice • Clumsy • Disconnected • Checked out • Diarrhea • Unfocused eyes • Blurry vision

bodyinsight Chantal Donnelly   Adapted from @Lumos Transforms 2017 property

Step Two:

Don't Try to Be Calm 24/7

CHAPTER 3

Calm Isn't Always the Goal

Wouldn't it be great to live in a world with no stress?

As I cross items off my to-do list, reducing my responsibilities to a manageable mound (or so I tell myself), I seem to be working toward a blissful future when all stressful feelings evaporate.

It's a popular fantasy. But is it a valid goal? The truth is stressors are unavoidable. They're part of life. Our stress responses are not only inevitable but also necessary.

Always being calm is not an appropriate goal because sometimes non-calm stress responses are needed for survival. I hesitate to use the word "survival" because it brings to mind visions of lions, tigers, and bears. As much as our autonomic nervous system evolved to survive in the wilderness, that visual is hard to relate to. People dismiss it as irrelevant in today's world.

Even though our current versions of survival usually don't involve wild animals, it still *feels* like survival. Work deadlines, leaking roofs, noisy neighbors, unexpected medical bills, hurricane warnings, surgery—all these stressors, and more—trigger cues of danger to our nervous systems.

The Goldilocks Principle

When people hear I study stress, they assume I'm trying to eradicate it. But I'm not so delusional (at least, not on this) to think we can rid the planet of all forms of suffering. Even if we could, I'm not sure we *should*—because life without stress leads to life without resilience.

It turns out too little stress on a person can have just as adverse an effect as too much stress. There is a "just right" amount of stress. Stress follows what has been called the "Goldilocks principle." Remember young Goldilocks from the story of the three bears? "Not too hot, not too cold—just right!"

The benefits of stress, when plotted on a graph, form a bell curve rather than a diagonal line. Maia Szalavitz notes in *Time* magazine:

> [T]here's a sweet spot of stress: too much stress overloads the system and makes life difficult, but having had too little stress causes similar problems. It may be that people who have been through just enough hardship are best able to develop their abilities to cope—and have a more firmly established network of social support—making it easier for them to handle tough experiences later on (2011).

You can't build your resilience muscle without some adversity. This explains why there's been a backlash against coddling children. We've found that so-called helicopter parenting—keeping kids from having negative experiences, disappointments, or failures—leaves them unprepared for life's challenges and lacking confidence in their abilities to cope. It compromises their personal growth and distorts their expectations of what life might throw at them.

However, when the pendulum swings too far in the opposite direction, you have parents refusing to provide even a basic level of support. They withhold assistance, advocacy, and affection in an erroneous attempt to teach children that disappointment, pain, and suffering are constants in our world.

Through the application of the Goldilocks principle, parents can find a middle point, allowing kids to experience life's struggles without yanking away their supportive foundations.

My Attempts at Eliminating Stress

Parents aren't the only ones who can benefit from the Goldilocks principle; we all can. This understanding of stress helped me find my own middle ground between frantic and shut-down.

After diagnosing myself as "stress sensitive," I did everything in my power to erase stress from my life. This was neither denial nor numbing; this was full-on avoidance.

My goal was a life of zero stress. I essentially "helicoptered" my entire existence, circumventing anything that might be remotely stressful. I safeguarded my calendar, careful never to over pack my schedule. In fact, if I planned two activities on one day—say, a doctor's appointment and lunch with a friend—that was a *full* day by my standards. I wouldn't plan any additional engagements, even if it meant turning down a potentially enriching or exciting experience.

When I started my own business, I refused to add employees for fear of creating hassle. I didn't advertise my services for fear of getting too busy and adding stress. I chose to have only one child because two would be way too much. After our son begged for years to get a dog, we got an extremely mellow, mature canine, *not* a puppy (way too stressful)!

I even curbed friendships, establishing what I thought were healthy limits by only allowing a handful of close friends and putting up a "no vacancy" sign should any newcomers approach. After all, friendships are a lot of work. They require time, energy, and maintenance, and they generate the occasional complication—i.e., stress.

I was allergic to stress and addicted to controlling it. I avoided discomfort, ambiguity, chaos, risk, unfamiliarity, and spontaneity like a pro. My boundaries formed a disinfected, hermetically sealed bubble of attempted calm.

Eventually, though, I had to admit my avoidance of stress was no longer protecting me—it was suffocating me.

I helicoptered and bubble wrapped myself out of opportunities, growth, friendships, and novel experiences. To stay safe, I stayed small. As they say, "Sometimes the strategies that keep us alive can keep us from living." (I have no idea who said this, but they were probably spying on me.)

Protective Strategies Leave a Scar

My instinct to (over)protect myself from stress wasn't all that ridiculous. In fact, that approach works much like scar tissue, which forms when our bodies go into protection mode. An injury brings inflammation and the repair brigade, laying down new connective fibers for healing. But if inflammation remains for too long, fibers get laid down in a haphazard, overzealous way—instead of the linear, orderly way characteristic of uninjured tissue. As a result of this overcompensation, scars become bulky, sensitive, dysfunctional, and inflexible. They may cause pain or restrict movement. They're trying to help. But they are the body's overreaction to injury.

I've seen countless patients whose internal scar tissue pulled their bodies out of alignment. An old knee scar, for example, can change your gait, causing low back pain. Or an injured hip can change your golf swing, tearing your rotator cuff. What begins as an adaptive, protective mechanism can end up creating pain and injury somewhere else down (or up) the chain.

My strategies for protecting myself from stress created emotional scar tissue. Their well-intentioned constraints made me feel stuck, restricting my forward progress and causing my life to limp sideways. Until I found the Settled Section, my stress avoidance was just making me stressed.

The Need to Mobilize

We know from the Stress Quadrant that a short jaunt up the y-axis (the Movement System) will give us a mild level of arousal—a jolt from our sympathetic nervous system, promoting alertness, motivation, readiness, enthusiasm, and drive. This is where stress sparks the kind of motion and action we want. Whether you're attempting to raise your professional prestige, top your best score, or write a book, you need some Movement System activation (fight-or-flight energy) to get the job done.

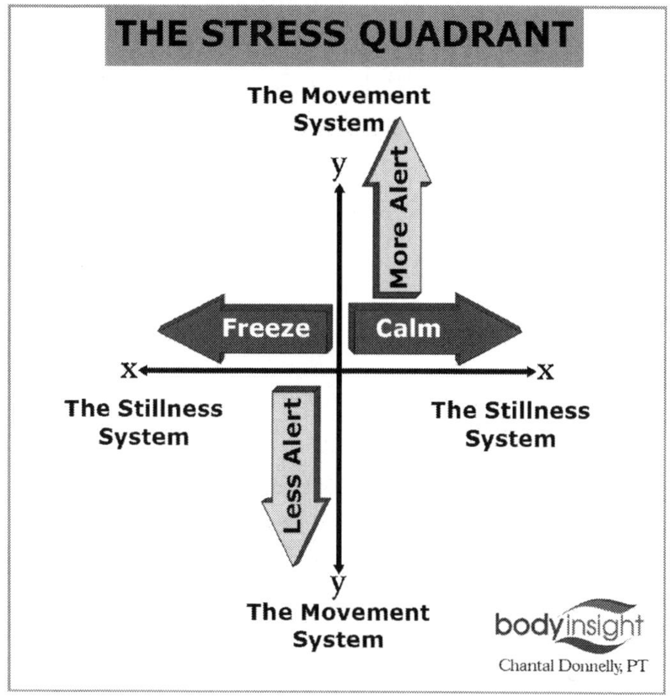

As we move higher up the Movement System's y-axis, we become more irritable, angry even. It makes us fidgety, restless, uneasy, touchy, squirmy, and on edge. These sensations are movements in and of themselves, but they also spur additional action. They push us to act (quit the terrible job, divorce the abusive spouse, speak up at the meeting, pick up the protest sign, or pack up and move), to take a leap despite the risk of embarrassment or failure.

Activation of the Movement System releases adrenaline, the body's immediate, short-burst response to stress. The body also releases cortisol, which gives us our slower, more long-term, brain-and-body response to stress. Cortisol comes from neither the Movement nor the Stillness Systems but rather from the adrenal glands—when a cascade of hormone messages from the brain's hypothalamus and pituitary gland tells the adrenals to produce cortisol.

Despite being the stress hormone, cortisol also plays a major role in regulating the sleep-wake cycle. Cortisol levels are at their highest in the morning, helping us wake up and get out of bed. In the evening, cortisol levels naturally decline in preparation for sleep. Since alertness is a fundamental property of stress hormones, it's easy to see how stress affects sleep and vice versa. It's also easy to see how stress can be the metaphorical wind beneath our wings (or, in my case, the needed kick in the butt).

Dr. Kelly McGonigal discusses the benefits of a strong, physical response to stress in her book, *The Upside of Stress:* Research shows accident survivors with larger spikes in stress hormones have better long-term recoveries than survivors with decreased physical reactions. In addition, studies of students at all grade levels demonstrate those who experience an uptick in stress perform better on exams than those who stay physically calmer during testing (McGonigal 2015).

When we're recovering from trauma or taking an exam, the increase in focus and alertness coming from our Movement System actually helps us.

Tend-and-Befriend

Until recently, studies on stress typically excluded women, with female test subjects accounting for only about 17 percent of participants prior to 1995. Dr. Shelley E. Taylor, a professor of psychology at UCLA, took issue with this (you go, girl!) and began examining the female version of fight-or-flight.

Taylor found that although men and women have the same biological reaction to stress (releasing cortisol and adrenaline), women react with less hostility and aggression. They tend to respond to external threats or stressors by taking care of their offspring and connecting with others. She calls this "tend and befriend" (Taylor et al. 2000).

On the Stress Quadrant, you find the tend-and-befriend response in the top-right quadrant, hosting a game of tug-of-war between the Movement System and the social engagement system.

Tend-and-befriend provides another example of how a stress response is a helpful strategy for managing stressors—and for survival. Caring for their young and forming networks of protective support and assistance will serve a group better than running off and leaving behind offspring or trying to fight a predator alone.

Although tend-and-befriend responses are predominantly in women and LGBTQ+ folks (Juster et al. 2015), men can have these responses as well—just as women can go through fight-or-flight (Taylor 2006; Byrd-Craven, Auer, and Kennison 2015). Variations of these responses depend on several factors, including genetics, oxytocin and estrogen levels, gender identity, degree of threat, and influences from a culture's normative gender roles.

The Need to Pause

Some animals freeze when attacked, feigning death and deceiving their predators. Humans can also experience the Freeze quadrant if we face a threat and feel trapped.

During the COVID-19 pandemic, an article by psychologist Adam Grant went viral (no pun intended) for giving a name to our prevailing sense of stagnation and emptiness. He called it "languishing." According to Grant, our universal "meh" was neither burnout nor depression, but a nagging feeling of joylessness and lack of purpose (Grant 2021).

Although I agree that in 2021, most of us were teetering in a mixed state—not collapsed but also not fully alive—I have a different theory about our collective experience:

We responded to the initial threat of a virus with an activated Movement System state of "fight-or-flight" and/or "tend-and-befriend." We organized every closet in the house, hoarded toilet paper, hosted Zoom get-togethers, and did grocery shopping for elderly neighbors. In short, we stayed busy and relatively active. It wasn't until later, when we had exhausted our supply of adrenaline and were deeply entrenched in lockdown, that we slid into feeling like caged animals, and the melancholy set in.

It's important to note, this slow slide into the Freeze quadrant was trying to help us. It was our adaptive way of coping with an inability to run away while the threat was still lurking in the bushes.

Of course we were stagnant. Venturing out into new adventures wasn't prudent. Even if we could orchestrate them online, our bodies didn't register these efforts as "safe."

Some call freezing the "pause and reflect" response. If you're recuperating from a debilitating burnout, the disconnected stillness of Freeze may facilitate your recovery. Like fight-or-flight, freezing is a normal, automatic, biological response that can be valuable and protective.

Why Calm Down?

Adrenaline and cortisol help us move, think, and cope throughout the day. Seeking constant calmness in our modern-day society (like I tried to do), comes at the expense of living a full and meaningful life. If we are to flourish, stress reactions must energize us into action and periodically paralyze us for crucial moments of rest. This is how the body wisely responds to life's hitches.

So, if our stress responses are biological and help us take action, stay safe, perform better, rest, and grow, why are we so focused on calming down and sitting crisscross applesauce on the meditation pillow? Why "keep calm and carry on?" If stressing out is so advantageous, why write (or read) a book about settling the nervous system? Well, we have arrived at the fork in the road.

Step Three:

Understand the Factors Influencing Your Stress State

CHAPTER 4

The Fork in the Road

We have just spent an entire chapter discussing why stress is natural and how it can assist you. But what if *your* stress doesn't feel the slightest bit normal—or helpful? Odds are your stress feels terrible and it's hurting, hindering, and harming you. If stress is making you unhappy, you are not alone. Moreover, you are not weak, wrong, or crazy.

If stress is a path, we have come to a fork in the road. Acute stress is where the path begins. Chronic stress is where the path diverges.

Acute vs. Chronic Stress

Acute stress is short-term stress. It comes from a temporary stressor with a clear ending: a stove fire, for example, that is quickly extinguished. Scholars and scientists agree that the body's rapid response to acute stress—its ability to mobilize for short-term problems—is helpful and adaptive. Physiologically, acute stress responses activate the immune system, decrease inflammation, and improve focus (Sorrells et al. 2009).

In contrast, chronic stress can continue for months with no definite ending. Even if the long-term upheaval in your life fluctuates in intensity, it feels constant. This is where stress gets messy. It is also where most of us live—with chronic challenges that don't ease up: the stove fire that becomes a house fire that displaces your family and disrupts your physical and financial security indefinitely.

On the one hand, chronic stress can increase inflammation, weaken your immune system, and crush your productivity and focus. However, as we have seen through the Goldilocks principle and the research cited in the previous chapter, chronic stress can also produce the same effects as acute stress—boosting immunity, reducing inflammation, and enhancing focus (Dhabhar 2009).

So, chronic stress can be beneficial *and* it can trample you. This is the fork in the road.

Allostatic Load

Allostasis is the way the body deals with stress. This process makes adjustments to the body's systems (immune, endocrine, etc.) to maintain a stable internal environment.

In 1993, neuroendocrinologist Dr. Bruce McEwen and his colleague Dr. Eliot Stellar coined the term "allostatic load" to describe the cumulative "wear and tear on the regulatory systems in the brain and body" occurring during prolonged stress. When the helpful chemicals produced during acute stress (e.g., immune proteins, inflammatory proteins, and cortisol) begin to "turn on the body," you get an allostatic load.

McEwen found that frequent, repeated stressors can cause changes to the brain, resulting in the dysregulation of various bodily systems. Allostatic load explains the strong relationship between chronic stress and disease. Through this, we see the connection between stress and higher blood sugar, cholesterol, inflammation, and blood pressure. These, in turn, cause increases in diabetes, autoimmune diseases, dementia, mental illness, obesity, and cardiovascular disease. Allostatic load is "the price the body pays for responding to challenges and helping us adapt" (McEwen 2005). Just like scar tissue.

I think of it as a snag in our evolution that our bodies and brains are still trying to work out.

Can We Pick Our Path?

Some folks get to the fork in the road and continue to meander down the "stress will help you" path. Others veer off in the direction of "stress is too much and will hurt you."

Do we have a choice? When it comes to stress, can we simply "think different" (as the old Apple advertisements encouraged us to do) and all will be well? Are we able to decide which road we take?

I asked my Aunt Sue this question over a nice pizza lunch: "Do you think we get to choose how we respond to stress?"

I was interested in her perspective because Aunt Sue is one of the most positive people I know. She is independent, confident, accomplished, and all about positive thinking. Things don't phase her much, and she seems to keep a smile on her face no matter what.

So when I suggested people don't always have a choice in how they react to life's demands, I wasn't surprised she disagreed. Her jaw clenched as I told her about the biological, reflexive nature of stress responses. (Oh, yes, I'm a blast at parties!)

"Everyone can change their mindset," Sue insisted, "and that will help them."

Then, in almost the same breath, she began telling me the story of why she never learned to drive.

When Sue was twenty-eight, she was living in Canada's capital, Ottawa. Up until that point, public transportation had been sufficient to meet her needs, but she decided it was finally time to learn how to drive. She wasn't anxious about her first driving lesson.

"It never occurred to me that I wouldn't be able to drive," she recounted. "I called a reputable driving school, set up my first lesson, and they came and picked me up at my house. And off we went."

Sue has vivid memories of that first driving lesson. She recalls being asked to make several right turns toward the main throughway in downtown Ottawa. She felt comfortable behind the wheel, despite being on a busy, fast-moving street.

From the passenger's seat, the instructor directed her to a picturesque area of town with quiet, tree-lined streets. Then a public transit bus appeared behind her. Sue's vehicle clearly displayed that she was a student driver, but when she slowed down to let him pass, the bus driver purposely pumped the brakes. Then he aggressively pulled up beside her.

"And this is where I start to have a very foggy memory," she said.

> I remember feeling that the bus was like twenty feet high. I remember it was so big! And I remember looking out my window, and the driver had opened his door. And I remember looking at him. But I remember nothing after that. I don't remember driving home. I couldn't tell you if I got out of the driver's seat, and the driving instructor got in and drove home after that. I have absolutely no memory after that whatsoever. I remember feeling so small. Just really, really small and looking at the bus driver—very conscious that his door was open. That is the last memory I have.

Aunt Sue never again tried driving. She relies on my uncle to drive her places. This is the only area in her life where Sue feels that a positive mindset hasn't worked for her.

"My mother always gave me this thought that there was nothing I couldn't do," she told me. "That was just my mantra."

Understandably, Sue felt perplexed and frustrated about the driving incident that led her to rely on others for transportation. "I just buried it," she stated, matter-of-fact.

A therapist recommended Sue try sitting in the driver's seat of a parked car. With her husband reassuring her from the passenger seat and the car engine turned off, Sue only made it through a couple of minutes before panicking.

"I have to get up," she told my uncle. And she never tried to sit in the driver's seat again.

Although Sue otherwise trusts that we can direct our thoughts to improve our lives, one of her own experiences seems to disprove that idea.

Two Divergent Theories on Stress

Aunt Sue and I are not the only people having this conversation. Stress researchers debate these things as well (they're a blast at parties too!). At the fork in the road, the research on stress appears to be in conflict.

In Chapter 3, we saw evidence that stress is good for you. Opposing research indicates that stress—via allostatic load—can make you sick. Substantial literature exists supporting each hypothesis, making it difficult to parse out the truth.

A majority of the "stress is enhancing" research embraces the stress-mindset theory. Dr. Alia Crum of Stanford, the leading authority on this theory, states that changing your perspective on stress can override its debilitating effects.

The stress mindset theory is different from positive thinking. Crum is not talking about adjusting attitudes or looking for silver linings. This theory specifically addresses your view and interpretation of your body's stress responses. In other words, "Does this stress response (sweating, increased heart rate, adrenaline surge, etc.) help me or hurt me?"

Dr. Crum was frustrated by messaging about stress being bad for you because she knew it to be an oversimplification. She and her colleagues set out to examine how changing people's beliefs about stress might change the way their bodies respond to it. They conducted a study designed to manipulate the conceptualization of stress among employees of a large financial institution. This study took place during the 2008 economic recession, and these workers were facing possible layoffs.

One group watched videos depicting stress as beneficial, and another group watched videos depicting stress as debilitating.

By changing people's thoughts on the effects of stress, Crum and her team were able to change the production of cortisol in their bodies. Because of these chemical changes, the group with the positive mindset reported better sleep and fewer aches and pains (Crum, Salovey, and Achor 2013).

McEwan's allostatic load theory doesn't deny the benefits of adopting a positive mindset; it just acknowledges that not everyone has a choice. Not everyone has the same inner blueprint for taking advantage of the mindset technique. Unrelenting stress can cause changes in the brain and body so that some people find a mindset approach to be inconsequential or out of reach. Stress responses are biologically and environmentally imprinted. Opting for a shift in mindset—a cognitive undertaking—is not always an option.

Allostatic load's more trauma-informed approach looks at the full spectrum of human experience.

Your ability to stay on the "stress will help you" path depends on many factors, including past experiences, ongoing adversity, socioeconomic status, family system, local community, available resources, healthcare, and coping mechanisms (McEwen 1998).

Untangling the Science

Stress *can* be good for you, and shifting your mindset about stress can be an important tool for building resilience and achieving success. But that is not the whole story. Stress can also damage your relationships, your career, and your health.

According to Dr. Crum, the purpose of her research is "not to try to argue that stress is enhancing and not debilitating but try to point out that the true nature of stress is a paradox" (Huberman 2022).

Unfortunately, the mindset narrative is often treated like an absolute truth. But because it is an entirely cognitive, brain-down approach, it is incomplete.

When we can't overcome a fear of driving, or can't control our self-sabotaging behaviors with our thinking, we wonder what is wrong with us. We struggle through our embarrassments and beat ourselves up over our shortcomings.

The expectation that our thinking makes us invincible misfires. It zaps us of our self-compassion—when self-compassion is the key to our healing.

This notion also emboldens us to be critical of others' stress responses—when we ought to remain sympathetic, curious, and compassionate.

And this brings us to a crucial point. Besides insufficiently addressing the body, the mindset method indicates a larger problem in our society: the belief that being pulverized by stress is the fault of the individual—a weakness, an attitude, or a behavioral choice.

What if we saw chronic stress responses and their concomitant diseases as symptoms of society's failings, not as evidence of how someone thinks about stress? What if normalizing stress could provide individual absolution and collective compassion?

In the next chapter, we focus on navigating the minefields (or should I say "mind-fields?") of stress and resiliency and discover how to dismantle any potential explosives.

CHAPTER 5

Stressism

Changing your perception of stress—from a threat to a challenge—works best when you are safe, when there's no lion in the room. But for many, the lion *is* in the room. And without a sense of safety, the mind is an inadequate tool.

Even worse, in hierarchical situations (e.g., many workplaces), and against marginalized or underserved populations, the stress-mindset mindset (yep, the duplication is intended!) gets used as a weapon.

To be clear, Dr. Alia Crum is not using her mindset theory in this way. I'm a big fan of Crum's work, and I believe the application of her research can be constructive. But it is not for every situation. Adjusting your stress perception works best when the stressor is something chosen, purposeful, and goal-directed. When we get to the chapters on exercise (Chapter 13) and pursuing goals (Chapters 22 and 23), we will revisit how to use mindset theory to reap the benefits of stress. But for now...

Shola's Story

Imagine you are working at a company where your boss belittles and berates you. Your supervisors are demeaning. They intimidate and humiliate you in front of your colleagues. When you complain about being mistreated, they tell you that you're too sensitive, that the stress won't hurt you and you should learn to "manage" it.

This company is using mindset jargon to dismiss legitimate employee concerns. What needs "managing" is the company's toxic culture.

These were the work experiences of Shola Richards. In *Making Work Work: The Solution for Bringing Positive Change to Any Work Environment*, he tells of his two-year struggle with being stuck in a "soul-destroying job," where managers bullied and gaslighted him, and he felt his "humanity slowly slipping away."

One autumn morning, he woke up, switched off his alarm clock, and noticed something different. He describes, "Instead of feeling pain, I woke up feeling nothing. My pain was replaced by complete and utter emptiness."

He elaborates on this sudden apathy:

> Absolutely nothing mattered to me anymore. My job didn't matter to me. My girlfriend, who is now my lovely wife and mother of my two equally lovely little girls, didn't matter to me. My parents, friends, and loved ones didn't matter to me. My happiness didn't matter to me. My life didn't matter to me. (Richards 2017)

On his drive to work that morning, he almost killed himself. He purposely swerved toward the freeway's guardrail before something inside him jumped to attention, and he righted his course.

When he arrived, he resigned from his job, essentially saving his own life—twice in the same day.

Victim Blaming

When it comes to our ability to bounce back from adversity, resilience expert Michael Ungar confirms that improvements in social, political, and environmental factors have a far greater impact than efforts to change people's actions and attitudes.

In his book, *Change Your World*, Ungar writes, "Resilience is not a do-it-yourself endeavor. Striving for personal transformation will not make us better when our families, workplaces, communities, health care providers, and governments provide us with insufficient care and support" (2018, 14). The allostatic load (or stress-related disease burden) becomes heavier when we're facing trauma, poverty, racism, or any other form of adversity.

Pointing a finger at people and recommending mental re-alignment as a salve for their hardship ignores that their stress might be coming from unjust, non-adjustable external factors. These systemic stressors—such as unequal access to employment, education, healthcare, wages, green spaces, or other opportunities—are collective problems for the community to examine, take accountability for, and change.

The prevailing view that these kinds of stressors are individual lifestyle issues is what Dana Becker calls "stressism." The discourse of stressism perpetuates these social, political, and environmental problems by treating them as inevitable (Purser 2019a).

Alex's Story

Alex was a typical teenager living in Milwaukee. A good, responsible kid, he worked at the local sandwich shop and saved enough in paychecks and birthday money to buy himself a car—a used 2010 Honda Civic. It was old and beat-up. But it was all his.

Unlike my Aunt Sue from the previous chapter, Alex successfully completed his driving test and got a license. He was, however, a nervous new driver. He was terrified he might get stopped by a police officer or get into an accident.

So, when it actually happened—when he got pulled over—he was a mess. While the officer explained to Alex why he had pulled him over (an incomplete stop at a stop sign), Alex couldn't quit shaking. His shaking was so pronounced the officer thought he might be on drugs and had him get out of the car.

Luckily, despite his nerves, Alex was able to walk a straight line and pass the coordination tests. Driving home, though, he choked back tears until he finally arrived in front of his house.

His father was furious with him for getting pulled over. His mother wasn't mad, but the incident kept her up for several nights. Alex wasn't able to sleep well either, and he failed an important chemistry exam because he couldn't focus and felt too tired to care. He stopped driving himself to school and went back to having his mother drop him off.

Mindset science would suggest Alex embrace the effects of stress—the bubbling of adrenaline and cortisol in his system—and use them to focus on the road ahead. It would suggest that stress helped him pass the police coordination tests and will continue to help his driving in the future. It would say to Alex, "Think of the stress from being pulled over as a challenge that can keep you focused, advance your driving skills, and boost your resilience. The stress won't hurt you if you embrace it as helpful."

Fair enough...

But Alex is Black. He has seen many examples of how a regular traffic stop can become a life-or-death situation for someone with his skin color. His parents warned him about the perils of being stopped by the police. His threat-detection system has every right to be in overdrive. No positive outlook or upgraded driving ability will change the current systemic racism making it unusually dangerous for him to get pulled over. If stress is related to discrimination, can our stress responses to it be reframed as advantageous in any way?

Science as Second Arrow

Alex's stress response was appropriate given the situation. The police officer was not wrong to pull him over for rolling through a stop sign, but Alex was also not wrong to feel scared. Racialized stress is an arrow to the heart. Telling Alex he needs to change his stress mindset is basically saying that racism, inequality, and oppression are his own problems, not the collective's. It takes the burden of responsibility off society and puts it squarely on Alex's shoulders. It aims a second arrow at his soul.

More crucially, even if Alex did change his mindset—seeing his driving stress as a valuable challenge—he would still have to navigate through the unchanged, unjust system. When stress is the byproduct of societal bias, reappraising it on an individual level doesn't do anything to address the fact that the lion is still in the room.

Individual Work for Collective Support

Alex and my Aunt Sue discovered that reframing our thinking is not a reliable, appropriate, effective tool in every situation. When a stress response is based on past trauma or ongoing adversity, thinking of it as useful does nothing to address its root cause. Body-based tools (like those in Part 2) are helpful. But why focus on self-regulation when there are deep underlying issues or broad systemic problems that require collaborative change?

Ronald Purser, a professor of management and ordained teacher of Zen Buddhism, warns that the prevailing stress discourse runs the risk of prioritizing individual comfort at the expense of social responsibility:

> Reducing suffering is a noble aim and it should be encouraged. But to do this effectively, teachers of mindfulness need to acknowledge that personal stress also has societal causes.

> By failing to address collective suffering, and systemic change that might remove it, they rob mindfulness of its real revolutionary potential, reducing it to something banal that keeps people focused on themselves. (Purser 2019b)

So, what good is focusing on ourselves? Does it reduce suffering and make the world a better place? Can those of us facing unjust stress find solace by addressing our nervous systems? And does the individual self-regulation of privileged folks somehow help carry the burden of society's unjust stresses?

What Would Shola Do?

After almost taking his own life on a Los Angeles freeway, Shola Richards walked away from his toxic job. Nearly twenty years later, he is a popular author, speaker, and advocate recognized for bringing kindness, civility, and mutual respect into the workplace. Richards is a leader in the mindset world, teaching others how to improve workplace environments through the principles of positivity, personal accountability, and appropriate individual mindset.

But Richards is known for something else as well. In 2020, soon after George Floyd's murder by police brutality, Richards posted on his Facebook page a personal account of his daily experience with racism, and the post went viral.

In it he explains why he chooses never to walk alone in his neighborhood:

> When I'm walking down the street holding my young daughter's hand and walking my sweet fluffy dog, I'm just a loving dad and pet owner taking a break from the joylessness of crisis homeschooling. But without them by my side, almost instantly, I morph into a threat in the eyes of some white folks. Instead of being a loving dad to two little girls, unfortunately, all that some people can see is a 6'2" athletically-built black man in a cloth mask who is walking around in a place where he doesn't belong (even though, I'm still the same guy who just wants to take a walk through his neighborhood). It's equal parts exhausting and depressing to feel like I can't walk around outside alone, for fear of being targeted. (Richards 2020)

Since Richards preaches perspective-shifting and self-accountability for improving the workplace, I asked him if he applies these techniques when out walking in his predominantly white neighborhood. He answered:

> It's hard because we're talking about a trauma response. And a trauma response isn't something that's voluntary. It's not something that you can just sweep under the rug. Usually, it's accumulated over a long period of time. I would say you can't just shift your attitude.

Richards, known for his big smile and big heart, went on:

> I know that I am going to be dealing with racism. I'm going to be in spaces where I may not see anyone who looks like me and, at times, that sucks. To be clear. So, knowing that's the reality I'm going to be in, I had to learn to regulate my own nervous system—my own way of thinking, my own peace of mind—to help me to excel in the spaces that may be historically uncomfortable for me. There's no choice. I wish there was. I'm trying to attack it from, "Hey, let's be kinder to each other." While I'm waiting for the world to catch up on my philosophy, I still have to do the hard things to help me in navigating these spaces... So I do a lot of breathwork. I do a lot of meditation. I do a lot of journaling. I do these things in a way to help me to navigate this world, knowing that it may not change any time soon.

And herein lies the difference between a generic stress-management program and the more comprehensive and nuanced stress manual we're developing here: the knowledge that we cannot advocate for ourselves or for others from a place of nervous system chaos. Through settling your nervous system, you find the energy and self-compassion needed to effect change—or at least to point you towards the path of most resilience. Only then are we able to use individual mindset approaches to contribute to societal solutions. Only then can we cage the lion and remove it from the room.

And then what? Do we become calm? If so, how? And when? Calm isn't always the goal, but sometimes it is. How do we know when to go there? "Keep calm and carry on" to the next chapter to find out.

CHAPTER 6

Sometimes Calm IS the Goal

Being stressed is *not* the problem; being stuck in a stress response is.

We need to be able to move freely around the Stress Quadrant, both for our survival and our happiness. Being resilient means having the flexibility to oscillate between alertness and stillness. Getting stuck is the antithesis of bouncing back.

When I found myself stranded in one stress extreme after another, I didn't have the fluidity to navigate around the matrix. I'd get catapulted into a nosebleed section of the Stress Quadrant and have difficulty finding my way back to anything resembling calm. This meant I was unable to recover from stressors. I was exhausted. Emotions consumed me. The constant uncomfortable sensations made my body feel unlivable.

Getting Stuck

On her podcast *Living in the Sandwich Zone*, Karen Osborne recalls "one of the darkest seasons" of her life: "I was unable to sleep. I couldn't remember things. I could barely get through the days. I was just treading water in my life, and honestly going under most days."

Karen, a trial lawyer in Los Angeles, ended up having to take a leave of absence. She believed her emotional instability was burdening the people around her, so she "almost completely and entirely withdrew" from friends and colleagues. Karen was in a Freeze state. (Osborne 2022)

Like other animals, we humans are supposed to move freely around the Stress Quadrant. When we hit a hurdle, we have a defensive response and when the crisis is over, we return to a more relaxed state and recover. At least, that's what is supposed to happen. Animals living in their natural environments don't get stuck in defensive states. After a threat is gone, they slip back into relaxation mode. We humans, however, tend to get stuck in fight-flight-or-freeze instead of returning to baseline, which is why we experience the health consequences of allostatic load.

Karen's involuntary freeze response was entirely appropriate (we will hear more about her story later), but she was unable to return to her Settled Section when the threats withdrew. She got stuck. Her defense response became what therapist Dr. Leon F. Seltzer calls "outmoded."

> As long as defense mechanisms remain involuntary, they can't be changed. But once you know enough to make them voluntary, you're granted the opportunity to alter or extinguish them.

> Of course, before attempting this strategic shift, you need to assess whether, in whole or part, the defense might still be required. Or whether (and frankly, much more likely) the defense is outmoded or self-defeatingly exaggerated. (Seltzer 2022)

When we're stuck, our stress responses become elevated and over-the-top (jazz hands!). Innocuous events feel threatening. Stressful events feel insurmountable. Our unsettled state spills over into other parts of our lives, and we end up attending to everything from a place of tension and alarm. Being stuck puts us on a path of "stress is harmful," and we respond to life in an exaggerated way that leaves us feeling spent.

Malfunctioning Alarm System

Stress experts often describe this stuck mode using the analogy of a malfunctioning alarm. An over-burdened nervous system behaves like a home security system gone haywire: Even a squirrel scampering across the roof sets off the alarm, and steam from a hot shower alerts the fire department.

When we're living in survival mode, we constantly signal emergencies even when there are none. Our autonomic nervous system becomes over-sensitized and anticipates danger around every corner. We become jittery and guarded, compulsively scanning our environment for problems. Or we become limp and wobbly, detaching and giving up.

With three family members in crisis, Karen Osborne had every reason to be stressed out: Her daughter was cutting herself and struggling with suicidal thoughts; her mother was in excruciating back pain and having trouble caring for herself; her father was battling cardiac issues and Parkinson's disease and was constantly "at death's door." Karen's frozen state was appropriate and justified, providing protection and recuperation through her body's primal wisdom to cocoon.

But when her family was out of immediate danger, Karen remained in crisis mode. Her alarm system had become hypersensitive and stuck in the on position. She couldn't sleep. Medication for insomnia didn't even help. She was constantly on guard, even unwilling to leave her home for fear of something happening in her absence.

Whether or not you've experienced a grueling cascade of stress like Karen's, you have probably experienced trauma—whether you think of it that way or not. Dr. Gabor Maté, a trauma expert you'll meet in Chapter 9, tells us, "Someone without the marks of trauma would be an outlier in our society" (Maté and Maté 2022, 20). These "little-t" traumas are what Dr. Maté calls "inner injuries." They can cause us to overreact, seemingly out of nowhere. We may feel as if we're out of control or losing it, surprised when even the smallest stressor leaves us feeling prickly.

It happens to all of us, but it can sneak up on you. It can *feel* like an appropriate reaction. We think we're okay, but then the grocery store is out of an ingredient for tonight's dinner, and we can't switch gears. Suddenly, the world is conspiring against us. We can't fathom ever feeling joy again. We freeze, unable to think of a substitute for kale.

Finding your Settled Section helps minimize getting stuck and over-responding. When your stress responses are no longer helping you, calm is the goal.

The minute we regulate and settle—even just a little—we start to get unstuck, and our over-responding becomes less frequent. We gain and maintain the ability to glide all around the stress continuum, broadening our Settled Section and preserving our energy. We see the world through a wider, more empathic lens, and we have greater latitude to reach for solutions.

From a more settled place, we can tell the difference between discomfort and danger. We can change systems that aren't working, alter our course, or advocate for ourselves and others. We feel safe enough to act, to leverage our stress responses, and to overcome adversity's chokehold.

What Breaks the Alarm System?

When we are stuck, our alarm system becomes overly sensitive.

When Karen got stuck, it wasn't a choice. She discovered there are times when you can pull yourself up by your bootstraps and times when those bootstraps have either been cut or covered in slippery oil. Either way, you're stranded.

So, what are the factors damaging our bootstraps, tripping up our alarm system, and keeping us away from our Settled Section? Perhaps a clearer understanding of the forces at work near our "fork in the road" can help us point our compass back towards home base.

Transgenerational Stress

Surprisingly, our stories begin long before birth. Stress influences us before we are even a blip on our parents' radar.

In his book, *It Didn't Start with You: How Inherited Family Trauma Shapes Who We Are and How to End the Cycle*, Mark Wolynn explains:

> The history you share with your family begins before you are even conceived. In your earliest biological form, as an unfertilized egg, you already share a cellular environment with your mother and grandmother. When your grandmother was five months pregnant with your mother, the precursor cell of the egg you developed from was already present in your mother's ovaries. (Wolynn 2016, 25)

Dr. Rachel Yehuda's studies on the offspring of Holocaust survivors suggest that adversity and trauma can be passed down genetically from generation to generation (Yehuda et al. 2016). The DNA doesn't mutate; the gene *expression* associated with cortisol circulation changes. These so-called "epigenetic changes" turn genes on or off, affecting stress sensitivity and the tendency to get stuck in stress extremes (Yehuda 2022).

What we sometimes attribute to personality traits (e.g., being agreeable or neurotic) are often epigenetic legacies from our ancestors. This effect can go back three generations. In this way, war, genocide, colonization, slavery, famine, forced displacement, or a parent's traumatic experience can influence our stress responses even though we ourselves never experienced those atrocities.

Conception and Gestation

At conception, the stress states of your mother and father affected your soon-to-be nervous system via the egg and sperm. While you were in utero, your mother's stress responses had a direct effect on your future resilience. A study of women who were pregnant and living near the World Trade Center during 9/11 demonstrated this, finding that biological markers for PTSD were transmitted to their descendants (Yehuda 2005).

So, you are born with a history—a stress blueprint, if you will. Certain determinants already set in motion before your birth, at conception, and during your fetal development can govern your stress responses.

As we will discuss in the parenting chapter (Chapter 19), after the umbilical cord is cut, you mirror your primary caregiver's nervous system from birth to around nine years old. After that, you continue to model the adults around you and learn from them, even as your own autonomic preferences take hold.

My Stress Origins

I come from immigrant women who carried a lot of stress. Who could blame them? When my mother was twenty-one, she left her country of origin, Egypt, after an abrupt change in government left her Catholic family fearful of religious discrimination. She settled in Canada. Her mother followed (somewhat unwillingly), starting over in life at age fifty.

My grandmother Nana, whom I adored, was always worried and waiting for something bad to happen. During her last years, she would sit on a high stool anxiously watching through her den window as strangers ran to catch the bus in the Montreal winter, worrying that they'd slip and fall in the snow as they hurried to work.

This elevated state of anxiety was transferred to my mother. During my childhood, Mom was always on guard, waiting for someone to take advantage of her or give her bad news. She usually assumed the worst of others, but once she trusted you, you'd see the funny, outgoing, feisty, loving, and generous person she is when she's relaxed.

The influential women in my life lived at the extreme ends of the Stress Quadrant. This wasn't by choice. It wasn't personality traits; it was their minds anticipating their past, expecting sudden disruptions and chaos. They expected home to become hostile at any moment, and their frayed nervous systems were cemented in defense mode. Just like me, my mother and grandmother needed a stress manual—to break the family chain of anxiety, worry, and hypervigilance.

Childhood Influences

Many factors in childhood can put you at risk of being on the "stress will hurt you" path. Childhood toxic stressors are called adverse childhood experiences (ACEs). They include growing up with physical or mental abuse, economic hardship, corporal punishment, lack of education, exposure to violence, parents or siblings who abuse drugs or alcohol, and poor resources from a disadvantaged community. ACEs have been associated with mental and physical health problems and can affect a person's stress response and their ability to reregulate after a stressful situation has ceased (Hughes et al. 2017).

ACEs present children with inescapable stressors. Under these conditions, children grow up with little opportunity to recover and prepare for the next stress wallop—reactivity becomes their only choice. "Experiencing undue stress as an infant may also damage the development of the prefrontal cortex, hampering the set of skills known as executive functions, which comprise working memory, self-regulation, and cognitive flexibility," explains author David Denby in a 2016 *New Yorker* article.

Into Adulthood

Life experiences continue to alter our stress blueprint during adolescence and adulthood. As young Alex discovered when he was pulled over by the police, it is constantly readjusting.

People enduring discrimination (whether against their race, ethnicity, disability, sex, religion, gender identity, or sexual preferences) are dealing with daily hits to their nervous systems. Over time, those constant cortisol-filled encounters add up. This means someone will already be shoved outside of their Settled Section just for being themselves. When a new stressor arrives, they are already at the edge of their tolerance level.

I see this play out with students who have learning disabilities. Children with dyslexia and ADHD grappling with grade performance have less bandwidth for dealing with the loss of a pet or a squabble with a friend. Learning challenges mixed with traditional classroom expectations already have them swimming in stress and feeling flustered and alienated. They can't handle much more. Perhaps this explains why kids with ADHD tend to be hypersensitive to social rejection. It is just one more hit to their nervous system.

When you don't have space in your system for additional cortisol, the stress piles up, spills over, and its effects are compounded.

A Pummeling of Little Stressors

Responsibilities and challenges can also pile up during our adult years. Stress stacking can weaken our ability to remain calm, even when the stressors—when looked at individually—are not burdensome: the construction next door, arguments on Twitter, a broken refrigerator, the sick cat, and the closet being so stuffed and disorganized that you can't get to your umbrella.

A cartoon by artist Will Santino paints a vivid picture of this stress stacking: The person in the drawing has a lemon press, and they are dutifully squeezing tons of lemons and making multiple pitchers of lemonade. At the same time, they are being pelted with more lemons. It's as if one of those tennis ball machines players use to practice their backhand has gone berserk and is clobbering them with lemon after lemon after lemon. The cartoon figure, head down in defeat, gives up on making the best of their situation. They are too busy managing the constant barrage of lemons! (@Will Santino Illustration 2023)

Stress is like this for a lot of us—one hit after another. We keep trying to follow society's advice and make lemonade, but there's no respite to be found. Our only recourse is to run or hide, protecting ourselves from the citric onslaught.

Factors at the Fork

When we get stuck, our alarm systems become sensitive and reactive. The fragments from our ancestors, the stress responses of our parents, the past and present experiences in our own lives all affect our stress blueprint and can put us at risk of getting stuck. The good news is that *the blueprint is not written in permanent ink!* When our alarm system perceives safety once again, our healing can begin. The tools coming up in Part 2 communicate safety to our bodies and minds. But how do we know when our bodies feel unsafe? How do we know the communication of safety is needed in the first place? This is the topic of our next chapter.

Step Four:

Connect with Your Body

CHAPTER 7

Soul Speak

Your body speaks its own language—a language without words. Learning to understand it and communicate in your body's vernacular will change your life. This chapter is a beginner's guide to the foreign language I call "soul speak."

Interoception

Scientists use a much fancier name for your body's communication; they call it "interoception." Your interoception is your sense of the signals, sensations, and states of your body. It refers to "the representation of the internal states of an organism and includes the processes by which it senses, interprets, integrates, and regulates signals from within itself" (Chen et al. 2021). These inner messages can be conscious feelings such as pain, thirst, fullness, goosebumps, face flushing, heart beating, sexual arousal, a tightness in the throat, or shivers up the spine—just to name a few. They can also be unconscious processes, like oxygenation or changes in pulse, or even your gut instincts or sixth sense. Your interoception is your "soul speak" (so to speak).

Having robust interoception means being a good listener to your body's messages. It is a crucial first step to calming your nervous system and one of the most important avenues to knowing when to do a settling practice.

Although Darwin and his contemporaries spoke of "visceral sensations"—feelings from the viscera (i.e. organs)—it wasn't until the 1940s that medical and scientific journals began using the term interoception (Plans 2019). "It is now one of the fastest moving areas in neuroscience and psychology," notes a 2021 *Guardian* article by David Robson, "with academic conferences devoted to the subject and a wealth of new papers emerging every month."

Benefits of Sensing

Interoception is associated with increased empathy (Fukushima, Terasawa and Umeda 2010), improved athletic performance (Seabury, Benton, and Young 2023), greater resilience (Haase et al. 2015), heightened cognitive abilities, better intuition, and decreased mental health struggles (Quadt et al. 2021).

Additionally, science writer Annie Murphy Paul notes that "accurately distinguishing among interoceptive sensations is associated with making sounder decisions, acting less impulsively, and planning ahead more successfully" (Paul 2021, 29).

Unfortunately, as a society, we often need to disconnect from our bodies. We live in an interoceptive wasteland designed to guard against overstimulation, preserve our illusion of self-assured happiness, or protect us from a dark hole of despair.

Famous for escaping dangerous situations, illusionist Harry Houdini disregarded his soul speak to help him pull off amazing stunts. These included being buried alive, being nailed inside an underwater crate, and being lowered upside-down, feet chained together, into a tank full of water. For Houdini, it was mind over matter. He always managed to ignore his stress responses and escape with flair and flamboyancy.

Then, on October 24, 1926, at the age of fifty-two, Houdini's body sent him an urgent warning. However, he was so accustomed to disregarding his body's signals that, despite a diagnosis of acute appendicitis, which required emergency surgery, Houdini decided the show must go on.

Ignoring excruciating pain and a raging fever, Houdini performed his act before a full house. During the performance (or after the final curtain—accounts vary), he passed out. Houdini was rushed to the hospital, but he died of a ruptured appendix. Houdini's body was tired of being ignored—tired of the illusion.

Like Houdini, most of us are putting on a show. To keep up the performance, we live an illusion, ignoring or hiding from the signals our bodies are sending. This isn't our fault, nor is it necessarily inappropriate. In our turbulent world, this is one way to cope. It's a dissociative strategy that is trying to protect us. However, as Dr. Bessel van der Kolk reminds us in *The Body Keeps the Score*:

> We do not truly know ourselves unless we can feel and interpret our physical sensations; we need to register and act on these sensations to navigate safely through life. While numbing (or compensatory sensation seeking) may make life tolerable, the price you pay is that you lose awareness of what is going on inside your body and, with that, the sense of being fully, sensually alive. (van der Kolk 2014, 274)

The Resilience Toolkit

I learned about interoception (and much more) from Nkem Ndefo. Ndefo started her professional career as a nurse and midwife. By the time I met her, she was no longer practicing midwifery and had birthed a program she called "The Resilience Toolkit." This course is a culmination of Ndefo's personal experiences, research, trauma-informed practices, and settling techniques. The Toolkit (as it's nicknamed) buoys participants and prepares them to manage trauma and stress—both past and current, individual and collective—by providing the necessary knowledge, support, and somatic tools for settling the nervous system.

The term "somatic" refers to the body. Somatic therapies are body-based techniques focusing on the connection between body and mind. These therapeutic practices take the body-up approach we discussed in Chapter 1.

I was so intrigued and impressed by the Toolkit program that I ended up getting certified as a facilitator of the work.

You can find out more about the Resilience Toolkit in the resources chapter. The Toolkit provides opportunities to incorporate what you learn here and to explore additional self-regulation practices.

The Guiding Questions

As Ndefo will tell you, her curated tools—though valuable—are not as important as the framework she created around them. The framework is a series of guiding questions that shepherd you through the process of nervous-system regulation. Without the questions, you wouldn't know if, when, or why you need to soothe yourself. And you wouldn't know whether or not a tool worked at settling your nervous system, so you couldn't use that information for future reference.

The guiding questions also give you the following:

1. Reiteration of the necessity and normalcy of stress responses,
2. Respect for the innate knowledge of your "soul speak," and
3. Agency to choose the appropriate tool for *you* and *your* situation.

These are the Resilience Toolkit Guiding Questions:

1. What is my current stress state?
2. How do I know?
3. Is my stress helpful to me at this moment?
4. If my stress is not helpful, what can I do to lower my stress?

5. (After doing a tool) How do I know the practice successfully lowered my stress?

Questions three through five will be addressed in Part 2. But to tackle questions one and two, we need to use interoception.

Question 1: What is my stress state?

Notice how this question does not ask, "Am I stressed?" As we discussed in Chapter 2, focusing on our stress responses is much more effective than focusing on the stressors instigating them.

This question is asking, "Where are you on the Stress Quadrant?" Are you frozen? Or in fight-or-flight? Are you stuck somewhere between fight energy and a freeze state? Are you feeling productive and energized—a hybrid of movement energy and calm?

Question 2: How do I know?

To answer this question, you will need to detect the sensations cluing you in to your location on the stress matrix. Reviewing the descriptions of fight-flight-or-freeze in Chapter 2, as well as the charts at the end of that chapter, will be helpful here. Cultivating an ability to recognize which state you're in is key to spending more time in the Settled Section, and will help us answer this important question. The remainder of this chapter is a guide to developing this soul speak.

Interoception Continuum

Some people are highly attuned to their body-sensing, while others fall on the other end of the somatosensory spectrum. Low interoception can come from trauma, addiction, autism, depression, chronic pain, or an obsessive-compulsive disorder (Chen et al. 2021).

For example, Tanya completely dissociates. She has a history of childhood abuse and was diagnosed with a dissociative disorder. This label doesn't convey Tanya's unique experience—or the resourceful, protective nature of her dissociation—but it does give us some insight into what low interoception looks and feels like. There are different types of dissociative disorders, but Tanya's seems to be depersonalization-derealization, which the Mayo Clinic describes as a "sense of detachment or being outside yourself—observing your actions, feelings, thoughts and self from a distance" (Mayo 2023).

"It's not so much that I feel threatened by going into the body," Tanya explained. "I've built up a mental image of the body. When someone says to me, 'connect to the body,' I'm mentally connected to the *concept* of the body."

Jill Miller, author of *Body by Breath* and co-founder of Tune Up Fitness, has the polar opposite relationship to her somatic sense: "I have interoceptive acuity that is really obnoxious. My internal feelings don't stop making themselves known. It's very noisy on the inside, which can be troublesome."

There is a happy middle, isn't there? You may be overly aware of your soul speak, or it may seem like a foreign language, but somewhere between noise and silence lies the conversational tone we seek from our soul speak.

Boosting Your Interoception

I am still working on enhancing my soul speak. Learning a new language isn't easy (especially as we get older), so I approach the task with patience and self-compassion. I make incremental progress week by week. I used to go through frequent periods where I knew something was "off" but couldn't identify what I was feeling. This rarely happens now that I've learned to settle my nervous system. I am better able to answer the first two Toolkit guiding questions.

If you want to get better at feeling the feels that let you know your location on the Stress Quadrant, there are several ways to go about doing this. Everything you will learn in Part 2 helps improve your inner sensing. But let's go over some specifics here to get you started:

- **Exercise**

  Exercise increases interoceptive sensitivity. Physical movement brings you into connection with the body. Brain imaging studies suggest that what makes elite athletes... well, elite... is their enhanced interoception, which allows them to optimally regulate their energy reserves for above-average strength or endurance (Paulus et al. 2009).

  That being said, even exercise enthusiasts can be cut off from their body's messages. Fitness fanatics sometimes ignore their bodies so they can reach their performance goals. Being focused on physical appearance or athletic ability is not the same as being attuned to your body's internal sensations.

- **Touch and Meditation**

Therapeutic touch and self-massage techniques can improve interoception (Myers 2018). Touch is a powerful way to communicate with the body. Your skin is a pathway where external sensations meet internal communications. Massaging hands "are not like pharmaceuticals or scalpels," states Deane Juhan. "They are like flashlights in a darkened room. The medicine they administer is self-awareness" (Juhan 1987, xxix).

Meditation can also enhance your interoception (Fischer, Messner, and Pollatos 2017). Particularly effective are the "body scan" types of meditations (Paul 2021, 27). These mindfulness practices take the meditator through an internally focused, step-by-step tour of different anatomical areas, usually beginning at the feet and working upwards to the head, shining a spotlight of awareness on each individual part of the body.

By combining massage and meditation, University of Washington professor Cynthia Price created Mindful Awareness in Body-oriented Therapy (MABT). This process facilitates embodiment through the use of therapeutic massage and simultaneous guided body-scan meditation (Price et al. 2019). She specifies, "MABT is particularly helpful for clients who are struggling to manage stress and chronic physical or mental health conditions" (Price 2016).

- **Proprioception**

Your sense of where your body is in space is called proprioception. Reawakening proprioception is an important part of pain rehabilitation and can also enhance your soul speak. There are many ways to activate your proprioception, including getting a massage, doing balance exercises (safely please!), moving slowly in water, stretching gently against a wall or floor, resting under a weighted blanket, and using body balls or other self-massage techniques.

- **Open-Focus**

Tanya, whose dissociative relationship with her body was vital for her survival as a child, began to heal from her trauma through a process called Open Focus. Designed by psychologist Dr. Les Fehmi and using the principles of biofeedback (electronic monitoring of bodily functions), Open Focus encourages awareness of the body through guided meditations. Its meditations start small, asking participants to first "imagine the distance or space" between their eyes (Fehmi and Robbins 2007, 36).

When you are deaf to the language of your body, you can only hear the language of your mind. The "separated" body has no choice but to constrict: "The simple act of moving out of narrow-objective focus is like relaxing a fist that has been clenched for years" (Fehmi and Robbins 2007, 42).

During our interview, Tanya recalled her first Open Focus meditation and how changed she felt: "It was so profound. I can't even describe to you the relief to not be in that state of constant thinking. Because it just turned it right the way down."

This technique emphasizes a specific attentiveness, allowing for a safe reacquaintance with one's body. The idea is to go slowly. After all, intense, overfocusing on our bodily sensations can backfire. Hyperawareness of internal sensations has been associated with anxiety, eating disorders (also associated with too low interoception), and other difficulties (Gibson 2019). The goal is to reconnect gently. Certainly, you don't want your communication with your body to become a yelling match.

When Your Body is Too Loud

Miller (with the "obnoxious" interoception) has experienced the noxious effects of loud, distracting somatic sensations. To quiet her overactive soul speak, Miller focuses on stimuli that are exteroceptive—coming from outside of the body.

> I'll concentrate on connecting with other people, especially my children, or even strike up conversations with strangers. I've learned to also use my eyes to look away from myself, focus my gaze on objects, especially at a distance. Using my limbs to lift, clean, or activate larger peripheral muscles can sometimes move me out of being locked into internal focused states. Singing and listening to music also helps divert me away from loud gut sensations or from hearing my mind ruminate about all the things.

Miller's approach turns down the volume on her sensations (and her mind) to improve the accuracy of her internal signals. A heightened felt sense is not the same as an accurate felt sense. You want your brain's interpretation of what you are feeling to match what's taking place under your skin. Having heightened body-signal awareness does not always go hand-in-hand with having reliable interoceptive "intelligence" (Garfinkel et al. 2015).

That brings up an important question: What happens when interoception is not accurately translated by our minds? What if we misinterpret our internal sensations? This is a *big* topic, and one we tackle over the next two chapters.

Step Five:

Decide If Your Stress State Is Appropriate for the Given Situation

CHAPTER 8

It's Complicated!

The mind and body have a close, undeniable relationship—so much so they often act as one. But, like most intimate relationships, it's complicated. Miscommunications can occur.

Jasmine first came to me with low back pain, a byproduct of her newfound passion for spin classes. Married with two kids, she sported a cute Jackie Kennedy haircut and a bubbly personality.

Jasmine found relief from her back problems after just three treatments, and I didn't see her again until two years later when she attended one of my online stress workshops. A couple of days after that, Jasmine reached out to schedule a private consultation.

During our meeting, her anguish was so palpable I wanted to reach through the computer screen and hug her. Her husband was having an affair with one of his coworkers.

There were months of ugly fighting. They tried at first to be discreet, arguing in the bedroom with the door shut so the kids couldn't hear. Eventually, though, the yelling escalated. When the screaming progressed to throwing sharp threats and blunt objects, Jasmine was left shaking. By the time her husband moved out of the house, her pain was an open wound. On most nights, she cried herself to sleep.

My stress workshop had resonated with her, and the body-based tools (which you will learn in Part 2) "took the edge off." But Jasmine was seeking help for a specific problem:

> One minute I feel like I am recovering from my traumatic couple of years, and then, I will be doing the dishes or cleaning or working out, and I get these thoughts of pain or hurt that come into my head. I feel my heart racing. I start to feel all of those feelings again. I just feel really frantic. I want to go to bed or eat something. I don't know how to stop those thoughts from creeping in.

I asked her, "Does this ever occur when you aren't moving? When are you simply sitting? Watching TV or reading, for example. Does it happen then?"

"No. Only when I am doing something, when I'm moving. That's strange." Her head tilted quizzically.

Jasmine's panic attacks never occurred when she was at rest; they were specifically associated with an increase in activity. Her body had become hypersensitive to adrenaline and cortisol. Memories of the fierce disputes with her husband were locked inside her body, and any time her heart rate increased or her breathing became more labored, she had a "faulty" perception that she was in a fight with her husband.

Movement unlocked Jasmine's feelings of upheaval and pain from her past relationship. This created a mismatch between normal, active sensations in her body and the way her brain was interpreting them. Even though her husband was no longer physically near her, the arousal energy required to do something—even as mundane as washing dishes—was enough to evoke a reminder of their marital altercations.

Brain-Body Communication Glitch

Jasmine experienced what I call a "brain-body communication glitch" or, in geek-speak, "faulty neuroception." Dr. Stephen Porges (of the Polyvagal Theory) coined the term "neuroception," which refers to the primitive, unconscious ability to distinguish, and react to cues of danger, life threat, or safety (Porges 2021).

In turn, the phrase "faulty neuroception" is commonly used to describe the kind of mismatch where the body is safe, but the brain registers it as being in danger.

During a mentorship call with colleagues from the Resilience Toolkit, I was reminded to replace the word "faulty" with a more neutral term. As the Toolkit's founder, Nkem Ndefo, pointed out, the body is not confused; it is protecting you from something very dangerous from your past. She suggests using the term "over-coupling," meaning two things have been paired together, and they need to be uncoupled for healing to occur.

Darlene's Story

Darlene came to me with constant feelings of panic. She felt jittery. Her hands were tingling. She had neck pain and persistent tightness in her chest and face. Darlene felt she couldn't control her body or her emotions and was always on the verge of tears.

During our first session, we talked about her past. Darlene's parents were alcoholics. She helped her father get sober many times and took care of him when he returned to drinking again and again. He passed away while in her care.

Since then, there had been many positive changes in Darlene's life: she got married, moved to a new house, and became the mother of two children. But, clearly, Darlene was hurting. I suspected a neuroception mismatch, but I wasn't sure where the over-coupling was occurring.

We worked together several times, getting to know each other along the way. It wasn't long before I could see how much Darlene's body was trying to protect her, especially in regard to parenting. She was an anxious mother—always worried for her children. The problem became obvious to both of us: Because of her experiences with her father, Darlene had coupled caregiving with unpredictability and chaos.

For her, caregiving was associated with fear and anxiety—feeling petrified about what might happen next and bracing herself for the worst. In Darlene's mind-body communication, it felt like she was caring for a recovering alcoholic in poor health instead of two vibrant kids excited to explore the world.

Darlene's body wasn't wrong; it had good reason to put her on guard. The problem was the over-coupling.

The Brain-Body Connection

I think of the mind and body like an old married couple: They predict each other's thoughts, influence each other's actions, finish each other's sentences, love each other dearly, and couldn't live without each other. This is the mind-body dance that Antonio Damasio calls "that intriguing pirouette" (Damasio 2021, 6).

But it is common for couples who have celebrated many anniversaries together to still have miscommunications.

Let's look at where the problem occurs. It's not that the body is mixed up. The communication breaks down because the brain *misinterprets* what is going on in the body. Information from your past is all the brain has at its disposal, so it analyzes the body's sensations using old data. This is where there's a glitch: in the brain's interpretation.

Researcher and psychologist Dr. Lisa Feldman Barrett writes in her book, *How Emotions Are Made: The Secret Life of the Brain*, "Your brain must explain bodily sensations to make them meaningful, and its major tool for doing so is prediction" (2017, 66). The brain is a fortuneteller. Its main job is to predict what is going on below the neck. Sensations in the body (i.e. changes in your Stress Quadrant location) happen first. The brain then guesses what those sensations mean based on past experiences.

The Past Becomes the Present

Research by trauma specialist Bessel van der Kolk and his colleagues shows the physical process of mismatched neuroception. In his book, *The Body Keeps the Score*, van der Kolk describes a study on the brain activity of people with post-traumatic stress disorder (PTSD): They placed patients in an MRI machine and had them listen to descriptions of the traumatic events that had caused their PTSD. Researchers were interested in the brain's response when the patient was "suddenly hijacked by images, feelings, and sounds from the past."

What they found was fascinating. Van der Kolk and his team observed that past trauma "activated the right hemisphere of the brain and deactivated the left," meaning the brain processed the memory of the event *as if* it were happening in the present moment: "When something reminds traumatized people of the past, their right brain reacts as if the traumatic event were happening in the present" (2014, 40–45).

Incongruity between the past and the present caused mismatched neuroception in the test subjects—just as it had with Jasmine and Darlene.

Real or Imagined

Brain-body miscommunication can also occur because of confusion between reality and illusion

You respond to a stressor whether it is real (e.g., having a sick child) or imagined (e.g., thinking your boss hates you). Often, real and imagined stressors overlap. For example, losing your job is a real stressor, but your internal monologue about the implications of unemployment ("I'll never find comparable work; my career is over; I'll end up homeless...") is just a script playing out in your head.

The brain-body can't tell the difference, though, between what is actually happening and what is taking place in your imagination or crystal ball.

Empathic Confusion

Another type of miscommunication can occur when we put ourselves in someone else's shoes. When our nervous systems are overburdened, empathy without boundaries can be a stress response.

My husband, Ed, is a music producer, and he occasionally manages record tours. Recently, Ed seemed irritable—not his usual chilled-out self. He was sleeping less and felt overwhelmed by his busy schedule. We were out walking when the reason suddenly dawned on him: He had been juggling dates for an artist's record tour and had embodied the stress of being on the road for three straight months. Ed's body was responding as if *he* were the one gearing up to drive to a new city every night. His mind empathically confused his own schedule with the schedule of the (much younger) artist.

This may seem like a trivial, somewhat silly example of how we take on stress that isn't ours, but we often have similar reactions when reading or watching the news.

When we are under a lot of stress, particularly if we are carrying some Freeze quadrant energy, we sometimes interpret pain felt by someone else (perhaps a friend or a victim we see on the news) as our own pain.

The numbness from this energy blurs the lines between ourselves and others. It's a type of mismatch related to our sense of space—our physical boundaries. Settling our nervous system allows us to feel empathy towards others *without* absorbing their stress and suffering. Our bruised and unstable world certainly *needs* empathy, but not a boundary-less version in which phantom pain and frozen helplessness only drain our ability to help.

Body Confusion

There are also conditions of the body that can miscommunicate stress to the brain, causing you to feel moody, restless, or irritated for seemingly no reason. You may not have a lot of external stressors, and yet you feel the tell-tale signs of a stress response.

For example, mild dehydration—a deficiency of just half a liter of water—can cause a stress response in your body. To find and follow general recommendations for hydration, take your body weight in pounds, divide the number in half, and drink that many ounces of water per day. Let's keep the math simple: A person weighing a hundred pounds (45 kg), needs fifty ounces (1.5 liters) of water each day. If you're approximately seventeen ounces (half a liter) short of your goal, your system signals stress.

The immune system and the autonomic nervous system work together to keep us healthy. When the immune system is battling foreign invaders from infection or injury, it asks the sympathetic/Movement System for help. This means illness, surgery, or a tooth abscess will activate your fight-or-flight stress response.

Histamine is released in response to foreign invaders, whether harmful or not. Such is the case with allergies. Stress and histamine have a reciprocal relationship, so your annual feud with pollen intensifies your stress, and stress worsens your allergies. This brings a whole new meaning to my complaints of being allergic to stress!

Estrogen helps regulate the stress hormone cortisol, so the waning of estrogen during menopause often causes an increase in cortisol production. This explains the irritability, brain fog, and stress sensitivity many women experience during this time in their lives. (I could write a whole book on my menopause symptoms!)

Certain drugs found in medications and other substances mimic stress responses in the body. These include caffeine and other stimulants, including over-the-counter medications with caffeine such as Excedrin and stimulant prescription drugs such as ADHD medication. Cortisol is a steroid, and corticosteroid drugs used to treat asthma or bronchitis can also imitate a stress response. I recommend checking with your physician or pharmacist to see if any medication you're taking could induce feelings of anxiety.

Foods that create gut inflammation can also spur a stress response. We will cover this in greater detail in Chapter 15. But for now, we will add nutritional factors to our list of potential sources of mismatched neuroception.

It's Super Complicated

A stress response begins in the body before it heads (no pun intended) to the brain. As I mentioned, thoughts happen secondarily and are translations of the body's messages. Because the mind relies on past information, its interpretation can go awry—like a game of telephone. These thoughts, these cognitive ghosts from our past, can augment and perpetuate our stress.

When miscommunications arise between brain and body, they magnify our uncomfortable feelings. These miscommunications can occur because of past trauma, wayward empathy, illness, dehydration, hunger, allergies, medication, or menopause. Any of these factors could signal danger in spite of safety.

When you don't feel "right" but you can't put a finger on why, when you don't want to procrastinate or worry but can't help it, when you know intellectually you "shouldn't" feel self-critical but still do, you have a mismatch going on. *Fortunately, resetting the nervous system with body-based regulation tools (stay tuned for Part 2) can uncouple these mismatches and realign the communication between brain and body.*

We've explored brain-body communication glitches involving Movement System activation. But do mismatches also occur in the Stillness System? Could the act of calming and finding relaxed stillness be misinterpreted as a potential threat? In addition to our instruction manual for getting comfortable with uncomfortable, might we also need an instruction manual for getting comfortable with comfortable?

CHAPTER 9

The Stillness Seesaw

Comfort isn't always comfortable.

Humans seem to have a limited capacity for embracing the good stuff. Like the heavy limb of a fruit-bearing tree, we collapse under the weight of our blessings. Best-selling author Brené Brown assures us this is common: "If you're afraid to lean into good news, wonderful moments, and joy—if you find yourself waiting for the other shoe to drop—you are not alone." She calls this natural tendency "foreboding joy" (Brown 2021, 215).

I call it the Stillness Seesaw.

Somatic therapist Kimberly Ann Johnson has also noted when good things start to happen, she automatically feels a pull toward the negative. In her book, *Call of the Wild,* Johnson writes about a technique she uses to counteract being uncomfortable with comfortable. She calls the exercise "Hold It." Whenever she notices sensations of pleasantness, she says out loud, "Hoooold it" (2021, 99–100).

The Stillness Seesaw is our tendency to teeter between the states of Calm and Freeze. Johnson's "Hold It" method is an attempt to maintain her ground and not slide backwards. This human propensity to tip the scales from the right side of the Stress Quadrant to the left is one reason we get stuck in stress responses instead of spending time in the Settled Section.

When I first learned about Dr. Stephen Porges's Polyvagal Theory, I was blown away by the idea that the parasympathetic nervous system (the Stillness System) is the birthplace of both Calm and Freeze. These are two contrasting states, sharing the vagus nerve and a lack of movement between them.

In the nervous system, "stillness" is an internal experience. It doesn't necessarily require you to be physically inert. For example, you can be making dinner—an activity that involves moving around—while in a state of airy calm or a state of heavy immobility. The latter is called a "functional freeze," a state of shutdown in which you are still able to participate in life's daily activities. Making lasagna for the family is going to feel radically different depending on which stillness state you are embodying.

Likewise, you can be sitting perfectly still at your desk and still be in a frantic, pressurized state. The "movement" is in your darting thoughts, racing heartbeat, staccato breath, and shoulder tension. In relation to the Stress Quadrant, stillness and movement are internal experiences not always visible from the outside.

Stillness Snafu

The stillness certainly *feels* different when we're in Calm versus when we're in Freeze. Emotionally, the distinction is dramatic. Calm's stillness is yummy, expansive, and light where freeze's immobility is yucky, contracted, and sluggish. To the body, however, it's all just a lack of adrenaline. The body only registers inaction.

Is it possible that our limited tolerance for calm stems from a miscommunication between the mind and body? *Is the Stillness Seesaw a neuroception mismatch?* If the mind-body gets confused by the many states of alertness (am I eager? or anxious?), then it stands to reason that it can get confused by the different states of stillness (am I tranquil? or immobilized?).

Unraveling Instead of Unwinding

Occasionally, I experience this slide from being calm to frozen—when my brain has translated slowing down and relaxing into a downward cascade of drained and shattered. On vacations where I'm just chilling out after a period of intense stress (versus more active trips where I sightsee and explore), I have intended to unwind—only to find myself unraveling instead.

The seesaw effect also happened to my friend Sam. She had fought long and hard to find the perfect location for her dream project—a retail store showcasing her art and ceramics. After being outbid or turned down for three years, she finally signed a lease on a location beyond her wildest expectations. But instead of celebrating, Sam started questioning her abilities and coming up with stories about why the space was all wrong. When I told her my Stillness

Seesaw theory, she immediately recognized her tumble to the left side of the Stress Quadrant. After using some self-regulation tools, she felt more comfortable with her joy over the new storefront. She could then hold her elation, feel her bliss, and allow those feelings to bolster her instead of shutting her down.

Our fear of calm is so pervasive that outward demonstrations of stillness can unnerve those around us. People often feel awkward during moments of silence or uneasy when we seek quiet time to ourselves. For example, Sara recently vacationed with her family and twice on her trip she stepped away from the flurry of activity to sit by herself and downshift. Both times someone came to check on her, concerned something was wrong. Her son, and later her brother, mistook her need for stillness as being withdrawn and upset.

The Seesaw Override

Workaholics know how to circumvent the Stillness Seesaw entirely: They don't stop moving. It's as if they have pole vaulted to the top of the Movement System and are hanging on for dear life.

Our culture's prevailing work ethic conflates being busy with being valuable, which leads us to question our worth whenever we find ourselves in stillness. Over-prioritizing work is a way to avoid stillness, thereby avoiding feelings of inadequacy. If overworking is your crutch, you are in good company. Dr. Gabor Maté, a world-renowned trauma and addiction specialist, also battles the beast of overdoing.

Maté was born in Budapest in 1944, coming into this world amidst the horrors of the Holocaust. As a Jewish person in Nazi-occupied Hungary, he was swaddled in his caretakers' suffering and stress. While Maté was a baby, his father was forced into hard labor by the Nazis, and both his maternal grandparents were killed in Auschwitz.

The war ended soon after his first birthday, but the harm was irreparable, and Maté's suffering continued. In the schoolyard, he was teased for being Jewish. Even his friends saw him as inferior, telling bullies, "It is not his fault he is Jewish" (Maté and Maté 2022, 311).

In 1956, his family immigrated to Canada, a place Maté still calls home. He became a physician and psychologist, got married, wrote several best-selling books, had three kids, and is now a sought-after expert in trauma and addiction.

But this confident and accomplished man was hiding internal wounds that only his family witnessed. Maté's children feared him, and his marriage was strained. He felt miserable, depressed, and alienated from everyone.

In *The Myth of Normal*, he writes, "My own workaholism as a physician earned me much respect, gratitude, remuneration, and status in the world, even as it undermined my mental health and my family's emotional balance" (Maté and Maté 2022, 202).

The documentary film *The Wisdom of Trauma* provides a behind-the-scenes peek at Maté's personal demons. One scene takes place in the studio where comedian Russell Brand tapes his podcast. Brand looks Maté squarely in the face and asks him why he has not dealt with his own trauma. Attempting to lighten the gravity of his question, Brand jokingly adds, "It's like Steve Jobs going, 'I couldn't get my phone to work.'"

In his signature matter-of-fact, soft-spoken manner, Maté explains:

> I was a driven workaholic doctor. Now, why was I a driven workaholic doctor? Because the message I got as an infant was that the world didn't want me. Now, how do you deal with not being wanted? You make yourself needed. So, if you're traumatized, and if you don't think you're lovable, my god, go to medical school. Now they're gonna want you all the time—when they're dying, when they're being born, and any moment in between. And that's highly addictive. Because you get the validation all the time. (Benazzo and Benazzo 2021)

Maté's traumatic childhood hammered into him the need to fill his time with achievement and productivity. He developed a deep mistrust of what would happen to him if he embraced stillness.

According to Porges, the brain can become leery of tranquility. Our past may be a constant reminder to our nervous system that calm *precedes* the storm. For example, if your childhood was idyllic until your parents suddenly announced they were divorcing, this may lead your adult mind to be suspicious of peaceful contentment. Your brain may say, "I was fooled before; calm isn't going to trick me again!" (Porges 2020).

Often called "perfectionism" and falsely identified as a personality trait, over-functioning actually serves as a coping strategy. As my friend Brian noted, "The underlying reason why people become super-competent—hyper-competent—is to avoid bad things from happening." Stillness might feel risky if you grew up in an unpredictable, disconnected household where you could only gain acknowledgement by getting straight As, doing excessive chores, and becoming a piano virtuoso.

Because they don't trust stillness, overachievers can't stop striving. They worry bad things might happen. So they avoid the stillness entirely. At least, they try to.

Like Dr. Maté, Dr. Miriam Zylberglait Lisigurski (a.k.a. Dr. Z) is a busy physician. During her time as an associate director of a hospital residency program, she oversaw the wellbeing of forty-five student doctors. Dr. Z noticed they were knotted with stress. Concerned about the rising rate of physician suicides, she sought training in wellness advocacy and orchestrated a mental health certification program.

When I met Dr. Z, she was writing a book on the topic of burnout and dealing with it herself (we write what we need to learn!). Burnout is defined as "physical, emotional, or mental exhaustion accompanied by decreased motivation, lowered performance, and negative attitudes toward oneself and others" (APA Dictionary of Psychology 2023).

Under such a definition, Dr. Z wasn't experiencing burnout per se. She loved her job, and she experienced no decline in motivation or performance during the work week. In fact, she felt better when at work. She didn't wrestle with a lack of motivation or with a negative attitude toward herself or others.

But on weekends, Dr. Z didn't feel like herself. She was tired and unmotivated. When we spoke, she explained, "I function much better under stress. I am almost addicted. On Saturday, I will almost faint on the couch." Come Monday, though, her energy would be back, and she'd be cheerful again. Her husband noticed her struggles. "He tells me to go to the Himalayas with the Dalai Lama," she laughed.

Fortunately, Dr. Z worked on finding her Settled Section: "I am more efficient now under stress than before. I have been able to control my extremes. I can use the positive aspects of stress better than before."

Perhaps we need a different perspective in order to understand the Dr. Zs and Dr. Matés of the world—those who thrive at work, habitually send emails at 3:00 a.m., crumble on weekends, and feel disconnected from friends and family. It is more than a matter of work-life balance. To my mind, overachievers are better than most at getting comfortable with uncomfortable, but they grapple with getting comfortable with comfortable.

Could our skyrocketing rates of exhaustion, work obsession, and burnout come from our inability to differentiate between calm and collapsed? Is this difficulty distinguishing between the opposite ends of the seesaw the reason we question stillness?

My obsession with my to-do list (a fixation I call "to-do list-itis") represents a similar stress response. Checking off items from the list allows me to check out—to keep busy, keep moving, and keep distracted. At times, I need this particular analgesic from life, but there are also times when my busyness isn't helping me anymore. It becomes a way for me to avoid stillness.

For Brené Brown, the antidote to foreboding calm is gratitude (2021, 215). This effective cognitive reframing targets the mind. To address foreboding calm in the body, settle the nervous system. This allows you to grow your capacity not only to sit with uncomfortable, but to sit with comfortable as well. Finding the self-regulating techniques and tools that work best for you is the antidote to the Stillness Seesaw.

But before we dive into the settling tools, I want to talk about one more way in which the body and mind can miscommunicate: chronic pain. This topic is near and dear to my heart—and one that deserves its own chapter.

CHAPTER 10

Chronic Pain

"A wall came crashing down on top of me," Amari Dior says, explaining to me how her chronic pain started.

Countless patients have told me the onset of their pain felt like hitting a wall—a sudden impact from out of the blue—a cold, concrete barrier keeping them from life's enjoyments.

But Dior was not speaking figuratively.

In 2016, she was walking past a construction site on her way to work when a partially-built wall slid off a support pillar and hit her from behind. Dior didn't even see it coming.

She didn't see a struggle with chronic pain coming, either. A kinesiology student on her way to a career in the medical field, Dior was a strong, athletic, energetic young woman who assumed her pain would be temporary:

> I thought, in three months, six months, tops, I'll be better. It's not a big deal, I told myself... And a year went by, and it was getting worse. And the doctors were basically telling me, "Well,

> you have three bulging discs... You have two pinched nerves..."

For three years, Dior hobbled from one treatment to the next: physical therapy, acupuncture, chiropractic, massage, and steroid injections into her neck and back. Any relief was partial and temporary. Her recovery hit a wall (figuratively this time!). The only remaining step, according to her doctor, was surgery. But Dior kept looking for another way to address her physical injuries.

She kept a pain journal, tracking her activities, thoughts, and emotions in an effort to figure out what triggered her pain. She developed what are called "fear-avoidance behaviors" around daily activities: She sat for only fifteen minutes at a time, drove for only short distances, and even stopped having sex. Her life revolved around limitations and "managing" her symptoms.

It wasn't until Dior stumbled upon the scientific findings on chronic pain that she began unearthing ways to heal.

Predicting Chronic Pain

A 2012 study out of Northwestern University looked at patients experiencing low back pain for the first time. The researchers running this study purposely did not examine the spines of these patients. They only looked at their brains. Using brain imaging, they were able to predict, with 85 percent accuracy, who would develop chronic pain and who wouldn't.

The participants who showed decreased density in the insula—a region of the brain involved in sensing the body (i.e., interoception)—went on to develop chronic pain. Researchers believe these visible changes in the brain corresponded to a decreased ability to accurately interpret sensations in the body.

Subjects who developed chronic pain also had enhanced connectivity in an area of the brain involved in motivation and learning, demonstrating that "the transition from acute to chronic pain" involves a learning process (Mansour et al. 2013).

Chronic pain specialist Dr. Vania Apkarian, who worked on the Northwestern study, noted that once pain becomes chronic, it is more easily understood "from brain properties than from the injury site properties" (Apkarian 2020). The brain rewiring associated with chronic pain causes painful sensations *despite* physical healing.

The Stress-Pain Connection

According to Alan Gordon, author of *The Way Out,* "Sometimes the 'pain switch' in our brains can get stuck in the on position and cause chronic pain. We call this neuroplastic pain" (Gordon and Ziv 2021, 5).

The pain may start with a physical injury, but then the brain keeps giving pain signals—even after healing occurs—because of predictions based on the past:

> [O]ur brains aren't perfect. And sometimes they misinterpret signals from the body. Neuroplastic pain is the result of this type of misunderstanding. It's caused by your brain

> misinterpreting normal messages from your body as if they were dangerous. The body is fine, but the brain creates pain anyway. In other words, neuroplastic pain is a false alarm. (Gordon and Ziv 2021, 24)

If this sounds familiar, it's because it bears a striking resemblance to how stress works. Neuroplastic pain operates like the brain-body communication glitches of chronic stress. In Chapter 6, we used the analogy of a malfunctioning alarm system to explain how stress responses can become hypervigilant in spite of non-existent or diminished threats. Physical therapists and orthopedic doctors use the same analogy to explain how pain persists in spite of physical healing.

The pain is not "all in your head." Your head (or rather, brain) is misreading signals from the body, just like the mismatched neuroception that sometimes occurs with stress responses. Walking or sitting—positions posing no threat to the spine—are suddenly activating the alarm, as if there's a major threat of injury or re-injury. The alarm system becomes hypersensitive—sounding continuously, unable to turn off.

Stress responses and pain both begin as adaptive ways for your mind and body to protect you and spur you to action. However, these can linger in spite of abated stressors or healed tissues (Hannibal and Bishop 2014). According to *Explain Pain Supercharged* by Dr. Lorimer Moseley and Dr. David Butler, increased sensitivity in the protective systems of the brain and body are to blame, "as though the orchestra in the brain is stuck on the pain tune" (2017, 4).

Dior's Journey Continues

Dior stopped tracking her pain. She found that journaling, at least in the early phase of her healing, caused her to fixate on pain, increasing her hypervigilance associated with the injury. Instead, she created a morning routine focused on settling her nervous system, strengthening her spirituality, and setting goals that "made life worth living, regardless of the pain."

She stretched. She used affirmations. She incrementally reincorporated activities she had been avoiding (a graded exposure therapy technique). She focused on social connections, gentle exercising, and breathing techniques. She started taking art classes, experimenting with new recipes, and working a job more aligned with her passions.

Today, despite the same spinal abnormalities on MRIs, Dior is essentially pain-free. She works out regularly and has returned to all her normal activities.

She also created Body Amor Wellness (see the Resources section), a coaching business that helps others find relief from chronic pain. Dior helps clients identify fear-avoidance behaviors, which can perpetuate pain through neuroplasticity. Avoiding activities for fear of injury or pain is rooted in the past, just like being stuck in elevated stress responses. When comparing chronic pain and chronic stress, psychiatrists at Yale University found both "share a common behavioral model of failure to extinguish negative memories" (Abdallah and Geha 2017). In the case of stress, the memory is past adversity or trauma. In the case of pain, the memory is a past injury.

Dior addresses other facets of her clients' lives as well: "Oftentimes, clients will go through life only focused on pain. They do not realize that other areas in life that make them dissatisfied contribute to their symptoms, due to mental, emotional, or spiritual pain."

Pain as a Stressor

Pain acts as a stressor. It's like salt on a wound. It can decrease your ability to work, thereby straining your financial situation. It can lead to poor sleep, making you cranky and affecting your relationships with family and friends. Pain is the worst kind of stressor—the kind that impedes stress-reducing activities such as exercising, sleeping, socializing, and having fun.

Patients with chronic pain often fret about it and scrutinize it, which—as it did for Dior—produces feelings of hypervigilance. Catastrophic thoughts torment them. This anxious attention, in turn, amplifies the pain. When your brain is on high alert, your nerves are on high alert, and it becomes difficult to tell if a muscle spasm, for example, is coming from injury or hypervigilance. According to Moseley and Butler, "When you're stressed, freaking out, or just don't know what's going on, your brain can release powerful substances that hype up the inflammation" (2017, 184). Inflammation right after injury is essential for healing. Chronic inflammation, however, strains over-sensitized pain systems, which gets us stuck in stress patterns, which causes continued inflammation. It's a vicious cycle: Chronic pain generates stress, which generates more chronic pain.

Bringing down the vigilance on pain can help break the cycle. This can be done with the same tools used to bring down the vigilance on stress. Same tools, just a slightly different approach. As soon as you feel an increase in worry, frustration, or despair about your pain, start using the tools we'll learn about in Part 2 to soften that reaction. You might still have pain, but you will send your brain a message of safety, so it can lower the siren.

Only after you calm the stress response can you effectively use your thoughts to change your mindset about the pain. Changing your pain mindset means reassuring yourself the pain is no longer physical in nature and will, therefore, eventually go away.

Chronic Pain Education

Understanding the nature of chronic pain helps break the pain-stress cycle. As I have mentioned, treatments for mental stress often benefit from body-up techniques. Successful therapies for chronic pain, in contrast, need to include brain-down approaches. Managing the thoughts and feelings associated with pain can help the body heal.

Like a stress response, a pain response tries to protect you, and its presence does not necessarily mean danger. It can be calming to know pain is *not* a reliable measure of tissue damage. "Hurt does not equal harm" is a common creed heard in rehabilitation centers. Pain-related fears, worries, and stress responses can intensify pain, but they do not cause tissue damage.

Gordon states, "By targeting the brain instead of the body, patients can finally get relief from their pain" (2021, 12). What he misses is that addressing the body can indeed help relieve chronic pain, just not necessarily at the site of the injury or in the conventional sense. Body-based tools for regulating the nervous system—the tools in this book—can make all the difference in relief and recovery.

My Approach to Treating Pain

As a practicing physical therapist for over twenty-three years, I have seen all kinds of diagnoses. Most of my patients who have unrelenting pain also have physical issues—arthritis, bulging discs, narrowing of the spine, joint degeneration, scoliosis, muscle imbalances, spasms. Sometimes those structural abnormalities are related to their pain and sometimes not: "When you look for structural issues, you're likely to find some, even if they aren't actually causing the problem" (Gordon 2021, 56).

If I work with a patient whose symptoms began at the same time as an emotional stressor, or whose pain fluctuates with the ups and downs of their life, I know their autonomic nervous system needs attention. Patients often have overlapping problems of structural damage, nervous system overprotection, and neuroplastic changes within the brain.

I help patients get unstuck—helping them move stuck tissues and move out of stuck nervous system patterns. Learning to address both their body and their brain has been a game-changer for most of my chronic-pain patients. Molly is a great example of this.

Molly's Story

Molly was high-strung. She grew up in New York City and still seemed to be clutching her purse and looking over her shoulder. Her alarm system was constantly sounding. She was hard on herself, always watched her weight, and obsessed over anti-aging products and cosmetic procedures.

For weeks Molly ignored the dull ache in her upper neck and shoulders. But one Christmas Eve, the ache morphed into stabbing electrical jolts down her left arm. She ended up in the emergency room. Months later, when she came to see me, Molly was no longer using that part of her body. She had stopped attending her weight training classes and was in emotional and physical despair.

The medical imaging of her spine showed an anatomical problem that seemed to pinpoint her pain. However, research has shown that people with image-confirmed spine disorders are commonly asymptomatic. An MRI can show you have a disc protrusion, and yet you can be walking around completely pain-free (Elliott et al. 2011). So, I wasn't positive Molly's physical issue was the root of her pain. I had a hunch something else was involved.

Molly approached exercise as if she were about to storm the shores of Normandy; she got down on a mat ready for battle. She approached her job with the same intensity. I wasn't surprised when she told me she'd had no pain while she was on a two-week vacation in Tahiti. We tried changing her ergonomic setup at work, in case her posture was aggravating her symptoms. But that wasn't the issue.

When I asked her what had occurred on that Christmas Eve, she told me every holiday is a painful reminder that she and her husband are estranged from their family. Molly had coupled holidays with regret and grief. Nerve irritation, along with possible brain changes, stress-induced inflammation, and an over-coupling of psychological grief and physical pain were Molly's main troubles.

Through our work together, Molly developed a better understanding of her hypervigilance and how it was up-regulating her connective tissue. I treated her joint restrictions and muscle spasms and taught her some corrective exercises. She received chronic pain education to help her understand her nerves were healing even though the pain remained. Most importantly, Molly learned to recognize when she was over-responding and how to settle her nervous system. She was able to better manage her work stress, curtail her fear-based thoughts and behaviors, and give herself some grace in aging. She was also motivated to seek out a psychotherapist.

Molly got better. It didn't happen overnight—it was a process. Her pain still flares up sometimes, but since she no longer equates it with harm, Molly doesn't stress out about it as much. Now there's some distance between her pain and her reaction. She calms her nervous system on a daily basis, using the tools I taught her—the same tools, dear reader, I am about to share with you.

PART 2

Building the Toolbox

Now that we have laid down a solid foundation together, we are ready to build our settle-ment.

With the tools and information in the following chapters, you will continue to broaden your knowledge of when, why, and how to access your calming nervous system.

The chapters in Step Six include settling practices you can do alone. In Step Seven, we will look at how others can be resources for settling. Step Eight will guide you when you purposely maneuver outside of your comfort zone to take on important goals. Step Nine is a summary of all the tools covered in the book.

Quick note: If you are not a parent, you may be tempted to skip Chapter 19. However, I recommend reading it nonetheless. Even if you don't have children and don't plan on having children, you were undoubtedly raised by a caregiver and may glean some insights.

Part 2 includes four key points in our step-by-step guide on how to destress.

Step Six:

Assemble Your Personal Tool Belt

CHAPTER 11

Before We Begin

We have finally arrived at the "tools" section of this book—happy dance time! It's been an adventure getting here, but it was important to put that foundation in place before building our settle-ment.

Thus far, we have delved into the benefits of prioritizing stress responses over stressors. We have explored the biology of stress responses and used the Stress Quadrant to understand our states. We have seen that constantly striving for calm isn't constructive since stress responses are adaptive and advantageous (unless they become excessive or we get stuck). We have also analyzed the factors that contribute to getting stuck: generational and individual trauma, childhood experiences, current adversity, our predicting brains, and physiological factors like dehydration and immune system activation. Finally, we learned the importance of speaking our body's language. We discussed glitches in brain-body communication and how they can be misleading. We now understand how to tune in to our interoception (our "soul speak") and determine where on the Stress Quadrant we have dropped anchor.

With this information, we can answer the Resilience Toolkit's first and second guiding questions: **What is my current stress state?** and **How do I know?** By using our body's sensations and signals to map our stress responses, we can determine their appropriateness and usefulness. This allows us to answer the third Toolkit question: **Is my stress helpful to me at this moment?** If the answer is "yes," then choosing *not* to do a tool is the best course of action. If the answer is "no" or "maybe," then the fourth guiding question will steer us right to the tools and techniques for settling our nervous systems: **If my stress is not helpful, what can I do to lower it?**

The upcoming chapters will help you collect a whole satchel full of stress-regulation practices. Most are body-based/body-up processes, with a few mind-based tools sprinkled in. Some are techniques to use before or after a stressful event (what Dr. Andrew Huberman calls "offline" tools), and some are techniques to use while in the midst of stress ("real-time" tools).

Although you can choose to incorporate the tools on a regular basis or on an as-needed basis, keep in mind that consistent practice every day or every other day can be more effective than a rescue approach—especially in the early stages of nervous system re-education. Practicing for even just a minute a day goes a long way toward finding your Settled Section. Steady practice broadens your stress threshold. In this way, it will take more to overwhelm you. When a tidal wave of stress comes crashing down, you won't find yourself drowning or thrust along the rocky shores between frozen and frantic.

For ease of reference, Chapter 25 includes a consolidated list of all the tools. There, you will also find a scannable code with links to videos demonstrating the exercises. You can either read through this whole book and then go back and try the tools, or you can try the tools as you go along. It's totally up to you—whichever approach feels right.

It Depends

My favorite question I get asked at parties is, "Should I use heat or ice?" (I know, I go to strange parties.) When you're in a healthcare profession, you become popular at social gatherings. Anyone with an ache or pain (i.e., anyone alive over age twenty-five) wants to talk to you about their shoulder, back, neck, or knee pain. Or their son's soccer injury. Or their spouse's hernia.

I don't mind. I like turning trivial chitchat into an opportunity to help someone. Unfortunately, when it comes to questions about healing the body, the truthful answers are often disappointing. My response to the inevitable "heat vs. ice" showdown is always, "It depends."

The phrase "it depends" has been following me since my journey into the healthcare field began. When applying to physical therapy school, one particular question on the referral form had me on edge. "Is this applicant able to manage ambiguity?" No! No,

I wasn't. I needed things to be black-and-white. Clear and concise. I hated ambiguity. Yuck! Why would they ask that! What could it possibly have to do with being a successful physical therapist?

The purpose of questioning my tolerance of ambiguity became apparent early on in my education. My cohort was a curious bunch; we asked a lot of probing questions. And in response, our professors—whether answering about physiological functions or treatment efficacy (like heat or ice)—repeated the same annoying two words: "It depends."

I'll never forget the time I was asked to speak to my classmates about massage therapy. My friend Tracey and I were the only students in the group with massage certifications, and one day we found ourselves standing in front of the class giving a presentation on the topic.

The room was cramped and sweaty and smelled like spaghetti sauce, turkey sandwiches, and whatever else people had just consumed during our lunch break. In this program, the students remained corralled inside the same four walls while the instructors rotated, so our group was rather accustomed to the awful smell.

When we got to the question-and-answer segment of our talk, Tracey and I—with big smirks on our faces—dramatically unfurled the sign we had made. On the backs of taped-together paper bags in big, bold letters read: "IT DEPENDS." This became our official class motto, and the sign hung at the front of the room for the duration of our intensive, ambiguity-filled program.

For understanding the human body, medical textbooks were a good starting point. But my patients taught me the only rule the body follows is "it depends." I could be mobilizing a particular area of a patient's lower spine that, according to every reliable textbook, innervates the muscles in the back of the leg. But my patient would feel it in their left shoulder blade. It seems that when it comes to the body, nothing's impossible—it all depends.

The same is true of hot versus cold: It depends. It depends on the situation. It depends on the individual. Sure, certain physical properties are at play. For example, ice decreases inflammation, so it's most effective within forty-eight hours of an injury. But beyond these basic guidelines, there's a lot of gray area. It really does depend. As much as I hated that answer in PT school, and still do today, it remains my go-to guide for choosing treatment protocols.

Play Detective

And this, my friends, brings me to my biggest recommendation as you explore the nervous system exercises in this book: play detective. Playing detective means using all the clues (i.e., your soul speak) to figure out which techniques work for you and which don't. You can't assume they'll all benefit you because it depends.

Just because your hairdresser swears by meditation for her anxiety, or your physician suggests jogging to decompress, doesn't mean either of these will work for *you*. There's no one-size-fits-all here. The trick to building an effective toolkit for stress regulation, emotional balance, and pain relief is to realize what works for someone else may or may not work for you.

So, put on your detective's cap (figuratively—no purchase necessary) and investigate. Determine which are *your* favorite tools. Keep in mind, their efficacy may morph from situation to situation. Also, you will probably need to modify them over time as you yourself evolve and flourish. Don't be surprised if, where you once responded to breathing tools, you now find eye movement techniques work better.

As you play detective, you may find one technique immediately and consistently helps you relax, while another has no effect. You may even find a technique makes you feel more anxious. This doesn't mean there's something wrong with you, or that the tool is defective. It just means it's not the right tool—currently—for you. Take what works and get rid of the rest. (Or at least put the rest aside for now; they may become useful down the road.)

Signs of Downregulation

The final guiding question for the Resilience Toolkit is: **How do I know the practice successfully lowered my stress?** To answer this question, we need to know what downregulation feels like. How do we know our stress has been reduced? Or whether it's been reduced a little or a lot? There are, of course, interoceptive clues. These will be different for everyone, but they often involve sensory elements. Look for things like softening, expanding, lightness, and warmth. You might feel more socially connected, patient, and hopeful. When you settle your body, your mind will follow; you may feel your swirling thoughts settle—like the white flakes in a snow globe sprinkling down and coming to rest.

Some additional clues from the body indicate a tool is calming your nervous system. Sighing, yawning, eyes watering, salivating, burping, and tummy gurgling are all signs of downregulation. Your body is telling you it feels safe or calm if it can take a deep breath (sighing), get sleepy (yawning and eyes watering), think about food (salivating), and digest (burping and tummy gurgling). Sleeping and eating are biological tasks we don't attend to well when we're in a stressed state. Those are relaxation-state activities. That's why the calming nervous system is called the "rest and digest" system. You can use these signals of downregulation to determine if your self-care is supporting you or is just another burden on your to-do-list. Whenever you engage in self-care activities, look for these signs to make sure you're on the right track.

At Resilience Toolkit meetings with my colleagues, we often start our sessions with a settling technique, which causes about a third of the room to yawn uncontrollably (note: you don't want to stifle your yawn—let her rip!). It's a funny sight to behold, and it often gives me the giggles.

Unfreezing

There is one final indication of a settling nervous system I want to share with you. Sometimes, when you're moving towards the Calm quadrant, it feels like you're becoming *more* stressed. You may feel yourself getting jittery, shaky, or agitated, like you're moving into the Movement System. That's because you are.

If you've ever narrowly escaped a car accident by slamming on the brakes to avoid hitting something, you've probably felt that crescendo of stress reactions coursing through your body. First, you freeze. Shock steals your breath. You grip the steering wheel, unable to move. Your arms lock. Turning your head seems impossible. This immobilization may feel eternal, but it only lasts a second before you're flooded with adrenaline. Your heart starts racing. Your breathing returns but in rapid, shallow gulps. Your saliva disappears, and your mouth feels like the Sahara. Your pupils dilate, and your head darts around assessing the damage. Suddenly, you begin to shake. You're not cold, but your entire body trembles uncontrollably as if you have a case of the shivers.

When you're coming out of freeze, you can't just stroll over to calm. That's not the way our systems work.

On the Stress Quadrant graph below, you can see that to travel from one side of the Stillness System to the other, you pass through the Movement System (the y-axis). This means you cannot go from the Freeze quadrant over to Calm without first encountering fight-or-flight. Which is to say, you will feel some type of increase in energy as you shift out of Freeze (Dana 2020, 16–17).

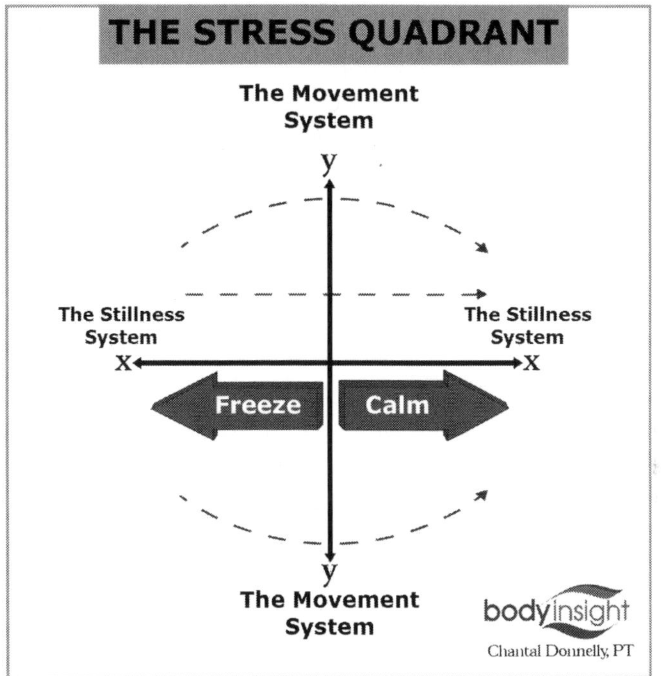

This doesn't just occur in humans. Stress and trauma expert Peter Levine describes this phenomenon in animals: "For the sake of survival, all the energy that was being utilized in desperate fight or flight (before it collapsed or froze) re-emerges explosively as the animal comes out of immobility" (Levine and Frederick 1997, 109).

In humans, the amount of Movement System energy we embody will vary; it may be imperceptible or even pleasant. But in the case of a near-miss car accident, it can indeed be "explosive." The shaking and heart palpitations are your body's way of insisting you attend to an immediate emergency. More importantly, it's a reset for your nervous system—a way to shuttle you out of being frozen.

I was telling a client about this concept of traversing through fight-or-flight to get to calm and he said, "Oh! I'm going to call that 'freezer burn.'" I do love that! But instead of leaving you scarred by frost like actual freezer burn, this journey through the Movement System from frozen to calm is a return to feeling. It's an un-numbing—a crucial step for returning to your Settled Section.

If you experience vibrating or trembling sensations while practicing one of the tools in this book, please realize it's normal. You were probably embodying some freeze energy that the tool melted, moving you into fight-or-flight energy. That Movement System activation may feel good to you (a new sense of wakefulness or aliveness), or it may feel overwhelming and overly uncomfortable (nausea, dizziness, or anxiousness).

Decide if the shift from freeze to fight-or-flight feels okay or "too much." If it doesn't bother you, continue with the tool. If the sensations are intolerable, try one of the following options for navigating this transition:

1. Stop the practice, rest, and try a different tool when you feel ready.
2. Modify the practice by decreasing the length of time you spend doing it or limiting the repetitions. (Sometimes ten seconds or two to three reps is enough.)
3. Modify the practice by changing the pressure, intensity, or range of motion. For

example, increasing or decreasing the pressure of a self-massage technique can make the journey through the Movement System less extreme.

We're going to look at novel avenues for helping our body-minds feel safe and supported. Please pace yourself. With the autonomic nervous system, less is more. If a tool isn't agreeing with you, stop. Stay in touch with your body's soul speak and follow the guiding questions, which prompt you to "play detective":

1. What is my current place on the Stress Quadrant?
2. How do I know?
3. Is my stress helpful to me at this moment?
4. If it's not helpful, what can I do to lower my stress state?
5. Then, after trying a tool, ask: How do I know if the practice successfully lowered my stress state?

I'm excited to share with you these practices for settling the nervous system. They are just a sampling of the techniques I use with my patients and myself. Many others exist.

So, let's get started! And please remember, when it comes to the body and treatment protocols, "It depends." Different situations may require different tools, and every individual is unique. Please, listen to your body.

CHAPTER 12

Breathe

Breathing is the quickest way to access your calming nervous system.

When Dr. Supatra Tovar became a practicing psychologist, she made a point of taking ten-minute breaks between clients. She found these breaks helped her engage more fully with each patient, improved her recall of their stories, and resulted in better sleep at the end of her workdays. But their primary purpose was to provide her with her own relief valve. "You realize, at the end of the session, how much you've absorbed in terms of stress from a client," she says, "and I would feel it in my body."

I met Dr. Tovar over twenty years ago. She was teaching Pilates at the same studio where I was practicing physical therapy. We became fast friends, and she ended up being the exercise model in two of my rehabilitation videos. She earned a graduate degree in nutritional science followed immediately by a doctorate in clinical psychiatry. It was a stressful scholastic journey, and calming practices helped her get through it.

Dr. Tovar now treats eight patients a day using an online platform. Her ten-minute cleansing routines take place in a small room in the bright apartment she shares with her husband and two rescue dogs. The techniques Dr. Tovar uses for her breaks between sessions are the same tools she learned for helping patients:

> I work with clients dealing with anxiety and stress and panic, and I had to be able to provide them with somatic treatments along with cognitive and psychological treatments for what was causing their anxiety. But the somatic treatment was how they could solve it for themselves, in a moment. So that's when I started to learn about breathing techniques.

Dr. Tovar's reset ritual begins with breathing. "When I started to do the four-six technique," she recalls, "that's when it really kicked in for me." This technique involves inhaling for a slow four-count then exhaling for a slow six-count. When we inhale, our heart rate speeds up a little, activating the Movement System. When we exhale, our heart rate slows down a little, activating the Stillness System. So a longer, sustained exhale stimulates the calming branch of the vagus nerve.

We see this in musicians like singers and saxophone players, who need to breathe with long exhalations. Studies on vocalists and players of wind instruments show improved stress markers after singing or playing for thirty minutes (Blasco-Lafarga, García-Soriano, and Monteagudo 2020).

It's not surprising, then, that Dr. Tovar's long, slow exhalations improve her ability to handle stress. Controlling your breathing is a quick and convenient way to directly calm your nervous system.

Slow Breathing vs. Deep Breathing

"Most of us breathe way too much air," says James Nestor, author of *Breath: The New Science of a Lost Art. In a podcast interview, Nestor adds,* "We think that by breathing more, we're getting more oxygen, but the opposite is happening" (Hyman 2022).

In a state of fight-or-flight, breathing is faster and more shallow, which can cause over-breathing and hyperventilation. Since many of us are in a constant state of high arousal, we over-breathe, decreasing the carbon dioxide in our blood. This may sound like a good thing, but it's not. Having too little carbon dioxide increases your blood's pH levels, potentially causing muscle tension or tingling sensations in your extremities. And since it's a deviation from your body's homeostatic balance, it signals danger to the brain. Nestor explains the negative feedback loop this creates for people: "They are anxious because they're overbreathing, overbreathing because they're anxious" (Nestor 2020, 177).

When we're stressed out, well-intentioned friends often tell us to "take big, deep breaths." In actuality, though, we need to breathe less—not more—to calm down. They should tell us to "slow down" our breathing instead. Nestor recommends breathing through the nose "slowly, lightly, and deeply" instead of through the mouth. "Just doing that," he observes, "can be really transformative for people" (Hyman 2022).

Dr. Elizabeth Blackburn and Dr. Elissa Epel remind us it can be "easier to change our breath to relax than to change our thoughts" (2017, 151). A study revealed a close connection between the neurons that control breathing and the brain areas responsible for panic (Yackle et al. 2017). Extending your exhalation tells the brain that all is well with the body. Sent through blood oxygen, pH levels, and direct communication with higher brain centers, this message activates your calming nervous system, corrects any brain-body miscommunication, and tells the brain that you are safe.

Inhale Primer

Since our breathing is so connected to our stress state, we need to consider not only how we exhale but also how we inhale.

When I teach breathing techniques to patients, I often see them inhale by bringing their shoulders up toward their ears and raising their collarbones slightly. This type of "neck breathing" or "upper chest breathing" from the upper rib cavity can send a message of danger to your nervous system. It's another avenue for miscommunication between brain and body (as discussed in Chapter 8), so our attempt to breathe away discomfort ends up backfiring and sending messages of distress. Movement instructor Mary Bond explains, "Upper chest breathing is linked with the part of your involuntary nervous system that deals with emergencies, the sympathetic nervous system" (Bond 2007, 78).

Inhaling from the upper chest activates the scalene muscles. These are small muscles found on either side of the throat. They run from the upper vertebrae to the first two ribs (my patients are always surprised the ribs come all the way up to the level of the collarbones). In addition to moving the neck, they are designed to help with breathing—but *only* when we're in a state of fight-or-flight. They are not needed for everyday breathing. However, because of our high-pressured lives, many of us feel like we're being chased by a lion and we end up overusing the scalenes for breathing.

SCALENE MUSCLES

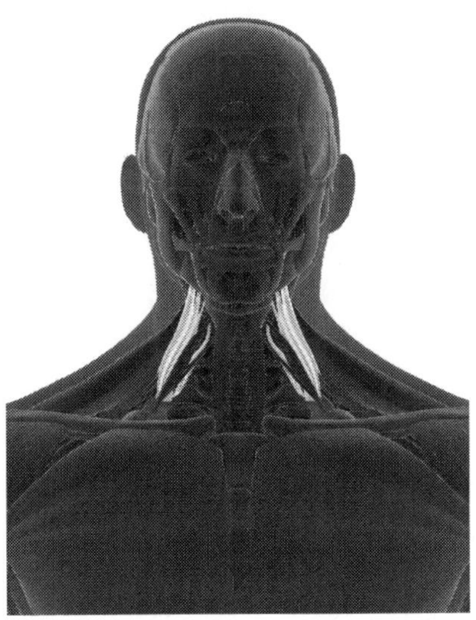

I see so many patients with tense, "always-on" scalene muscles. Research confirms there is a strong correlation between psychological stress and neck pain (Ortego et al. 2016). It's like the feedback loop that Nestor described: We chest breathe when we're stressed, and our chest breathing causes stress.

Improving Inhalation

In Chapter 14, we'll cover stretching, including how to relax your scalene muscles. But we won't need to stretch them as much if we can learn to stop upper-chest breathing and give our neck muscles a much-needed break.

In Pilates we talk about "lateral rib breathing," and in yoga the focus is on diaphragmatic or "belly breathing." Both of these describe the lower area of the torso which is a good place to target for inhalation. I like the term "lateral rib breathing" because it cues three-dimensional respiration, reminding us that the ribs wrap around the lungs from front to back. I also like the term "diaphragmatic breathing" because it emphasizes a dropping diaphragm. A combination of breathing from the lower ribs *and* the lower belly is what I would call "Settled Section breathing."

It's important to have a ribcage that moves properly because the lungs inflate *after* the ribcage expands—not the other way around. During inhalation, the muscles between the ribs contract, pulling the ribcage upward and outward. This creates space in the chest cavity, allowing the lungs to expand and fill with air. At the same time, the diaphragm contracts and moves *downward*, increasing the volume of the chest cavity even further and helping the lungs fill with air. When you breathe from your lower ribcage and abdomen instead of your upper chest, enough air comes in and the scalenes don't need to participate.

If keeping your neck relaxed while inhaling seems physically impossible, you may need to increase your ribcage mobility. Not surprisingly, mid-spine and rib-cage stiffness is associated with emotional tension. Flexibility in the spine and ribcage helps increase oxygen efficiency by helping the diaphragm—again, not the scalene muscles—do the job of inhalation. The following exercises can help you improve your spine and ribcage dynamics.

Rotation Reset

I adapted this exercise from a Tai chi warm-up. It helps improve mid-back mobility, leading to better nervous system regulation and better breathing. This is particularly great to do if you've been sitting for more than an hour. I call it "rotation reset." The QR code in this book's last chapter will give you video access to all the exercises in this book, including this one:

- Stand with your feet hip-width apart.
- Bend your knees slightly and be sure to keep them unlocked throughout the exercise.
- With your arms hanging loosely by your sides, rotate your torso so that your arms swing freely. You should be twisting from side to side with the movement originating in the mid-back area, just below the bottom of your shoulder blades.

- Let your head follow the movement, looking left, right, left, right.
- Your arms can wrap around your lower back and abdomen as they swing. In Tai chi, this motion of the arms slapping the body is called "drumming."

Ten times is usually a good number of repetitions, but there's no magic number. You can repeat this back-and-forth movement as many times as you like.

Pay attention to how this exercise makes you feel. You may notice an increase in energy or positive mood, but don't take my word for it. Put on that detective cap! Use it to get in touch with whether or not more mid-back mobility is something your body likes.

Ribcage Re-education

Now that you have improved your thoracic range of motion, let's work on ribcage mobility.

- Sit or stand in front of a mirror; be sure you can see yourself from the waist up.
- Fold a towel lengthwise and wrap it around your *lower* ribcage, just under the chest and above the belly button.
- Cross your arms in front of you and grab the edges of the towel so that your left hand grabs the right end of the towel, and your right hand grabs the left end of the towel.
- Pull on the towel so that it becomes more snug around your body. Relax your shoulders.
- As you inhale, feel your ribcage pushing into the towel. This resistance encourages your ribs to

open up. Notice the circumference of the towel expanding. Feel your ribcage open up in both the front and back of your body. Try to keep your neck as relaxed as possible, using the mirror to make sure your collarbones don't elevate when you inhale (this may take some practice).

- As you exhale, *gently* pull the towel more snugly around your torso. A full closing-down of the ribs (I think of it as "funneling" down) aids in pH balance and long exhalations. Use the towel as a tactile message, softly encouraging this movement.

Try this a couple of times to educate your ribcage on its newfound mobility.

Sitting as Stress

Sitting has been called "the new smoking." Our sedentary lifestyles are the problem, not sitting per se. Still, let's face it, we spend a lot of time sitting. We sit to drive, to watch TV, to socialize over coffee, and, of course, to use our computers. It's the bulk of what makes us so inactive.

Spending hours slung into a chair decreases your ability to regulate your nervous system in two significant ways:

1. It tightens up the middle of the back.

Interestingly, the middle of the spine is also where the fight-or-flight nervous system originates. I think of the Movement System as being "housed" in the spine. My theory is that all the sitting we do compresses and restricts the arousal energy of the Movement System, putting us into a more frozen state.

It's just a theory, but it may explain why desk jobs can be so stressful and why they often lead to mid-day lethargy and brain fog. The activation energy of the sympathetic nervous system is on hold—locked inside a tight thoracic spine.

2. It limits ribcage range of motion, which restricts breathing. If breathing is a freeway to calm, you can see how mid-back and ribcage mobility is going to be important.

Sitting Posture

Because slouching inhibits ribcage mobility and therefore breathing, your sitting posture may be adding to your stress. If your spine is rounded while you sit, it doesn't matter how pliable your ribcage is—you won't be able to use that freedom of motion. After you improve your ribcage extensibility (via the aforementioned exercises), be mindful of posture so you benefit from your new mobility when seated.

The most important aspect of proper sitting posture is the position of the pelvis. Getting it right automatically aligns your torso, shoulders, and head. To find the proper positioning for your pelvis when sitting, try the following technique:

Sitz-Bones Walk Back

- From a seated position, put your hands under your buttocks and find your "sitz bones," the bones sticking out at the base of your pelvis.
- Once you have found them, "walk" one side back and then the other, towards the back of your chair. This should increase the natural arch in the small

of your back. Slouching, on the other hand, will flatten that arch.

You may notice this automatically opens up your shoulders. If your ribcage feels like it's now jutting forward in front of your pelvis, draw it back and down so it's in line with your pelvis instead. Flaring the ribs is just as ill-advised as collapsing them. You want shoulders over ribcage over pelvis.

Now you are in the perfect alignment for making the most of your breathing and ribcage mechanics!

Not Just for Calming the Nervous System

Breathing techniques are not just for finding tranquility. They can also move us up the Movement System (y-axis). When we need more focus and energy, we can use breathing to turn up our alertness volume. In fact, we can consciously manipulate our breath to adjust our stress responses to the appropriate level—for more calmness or more arousal.

For instance, Nestor describes what happens when you plug the left side of your nose and only inhale through your right nostril:

> Circulation speeds up, your body gets hotter, and cortisol levels, blood pressure, and heart rate all increase. This happens because breathing through the right side of the nose activates the sympathetic nervous system, the 'fight or flight' mechanism that puts the body in a more elevated state of alertness and readiness. (Nestor 2020, 41)

Up-Breathing Exercise

Right Nostril Breathing

We can use this physiological breathing phenomenon to moderate our nervous system states. Here's how it works: If you feel lethargic, are having trouble getting going in the morning, or need to increase your energy and alertness, you can add some sympathetic nervous system juice to your system by gently blocking your left nostril and inhaling and exhaling three to ten times through the right side of your nose. Try it and see if you can feel your body becoming revitalized.

Calming the Nervous System Through Breathing

Down-Breathing Exercises

Exercise 1 - Left Nostril Breathing

Left-nostril breathing (with the right side of the nose blocked) does the opposite of right-nostril breathing. In comparing the two techniques, Nestor remarks that the left nostril "works as a kind of brake system to the right nostril's accelerator." Taking in air via the left nasal passageway is a direct line to the ventral branch of the vagus nerve (i.e., the calming nervous system). He explains that breathing this way "lowers temperature and blood pressure, cools the body, and reduces anxiety" (Nestor 2020, 41–42).

Block your right nostril with your right hand. Slowly inhale and exhale through only your left nostril for three to ten breath cycles. Pay attention to how this feels for you.

Most people find breathing exercises to be highly effective, but for some this increased focus on breathing can increase anxiety. Please remember: it depends. Try it out. Don't forget to play detective by checking in with your body to see which techniques work best for you.

Exercise 2 - Long Exhalation Breathing

As you're figuring out which exercises suit you best, consider trying Dr. Tovar's favorite breathing technique:

Inhale slowly for a count of four and exhale slowly for a count of six. Ideally, you would breathe through your nose, but if your sinuses are blocked or you prefer to breathe through your mouth, that's fine too. This practice slows down your breath to approximately six in-and-out breath cycles per minute. Biofeedback studies have shown this to be the optimal respiration speed for inducing a calming effect (Zaccaro et al. 2018).

Repeat three to ten times.

Some people prefer to inhale for three counts instead of four. Play around with what works best for you. Just make sure your exhalation is longer than your inhalation and try to keep your neck muscles out of it by avoiding chest breathing.

Exercise 3 - Physiological Sigh

Dr. Andrew Huberman has studied the "physiological sigh," a breathing pattern consisting of two back-to-back short inhalations followed by a long exhalation. This technique stimulates a relaxed response, and the double inhalation allows for additional opening of the lungs. Practicing the physiological sigh for five minutes a day has been shown to produce greater improvements in mood than using breathing techniques that don't emphasize longer exhalations (Balban et al 2023).

You've probably noticed the physiological sigh in children or pets because humans and animals do this type of breathing naturally during sleep and in times of stress (Huberman 2021). Luckily, as with all breathing tools, we can take advantage of this natural process and harness our innate ability to self-regulate—by consciously using it when we need to settle ourselves:

Inhale twice through your nose (short, back-to-back inhalations). Exhale once through your mouth sloooowly—for as long as possible. You only need to repeat this sequence two or three times. Huberman explains in *Scientific American*, "A physiological sigh, two or three times, is the fastest way that we are aware of to bring the level of autonomic arousal back down to baseline" (Wapner 2020).

Breathing is an expeditious, accessible, and efficient (not to mention free of charge!) tool that can be used to help your brain calm your body before, during, or after a stressful event. If you use a breathing app, be sure to incorporate what you learned in this chapter to improve its effectiveness.

And now that you have learned to move your ribcage, let's talk about moving the rest of your body.

CHAPTER 13

Move

Exercise is both friend and foe. It is both stressor and stress reliever.

You might expect a chapter on movement in a book by a physical therapist to urge you to "get off the couch." However, if exercising has been historically difficult for you, the pressure to do it can lead to more stress. And I'm trying to reduce your stress, not give you more.

Besides, you already know exercise is good for you. We don't need to belabor the point. There's a wealth of scientific literature out there demonstrating the benefits of physical activity: improved heart and lung health, better sleep, increased memory, decreased depression, clearer thinking, longer lifespan, etc.

What you may not know is most of these benefits are related to the fact that exercise improves stress management. In her book, *The Joy of Movement*, research psychologist Dr. Kelly McGonigal describes this:

> In humans, exercising three times a week for six weeks increases neural connections among areas of the brain that calm anxiety. Regular physical activity also modifies the default state of the nervous system so that it becomes more balanced and less prone to fight, flight, or fright. (2019, 62)

But what if you can't exercise three times a week for six weeks? Maybe you have an illness or injury. Maybe you can't get to the gym, and it isn't safe to walk around your neighborhood. Or maybe you have an autoimmune disease, and exercise exacerbates your symptoms, reducing your ability to function. Or you're juggling two jobs and three kids, and just getting by is all you can focus on.

Luckily, the benefits of exercise are available to everyone, even those who can't do burpees or sun salutations. This chapter explores theories on how exercise reduces stress, why exercise might not feel good to you, and how to get the most out of exercise's benefits—whether you are exercise-averse or a fitness fanatic. For those who can't exercise in the traditional sense, I offer other strategies so you can still take advantage of movement and all its perks.

How Exercise Helps with Stress

Knowing that exercise alleviates stress is great, but knowing *how* exercise alleviates stress might be more helpful. Why does physical activity improve nervous system regulation? Understanding the mechanisms behind the benefits can help you find ways of incorporating exercise into your life—even if you have an aversion to exercise.

1. Exercise Monopolizes Energy

Exercise helps us manage stress responses in some surprising ways. The first has to do with energy—not the kind that propels your car but the type that propels your body.

The Hadza tribe in northern Tanzania is one of the few remaining hunter-gatherer tribes on Earth. To study their habits, anthropologist and researcher Dr. Herman Pontzer lived among them "in small camps scattered about the rugged, semiarid savanna..." The Hadza do not grow food, use machines, or have electricity. The men climb thirty-foot baobab trees to pilfer honey from beehives and walk for miles across the hot savanna to hunt wild animals. The women walk approximately five miles a day, often carrying children in slings on their backs. They spend hours picking berries and using sticks to dig for tubers in the rocky, compact soil. The Hadza's foraging tasks require them to do more exercise in a typical day than most of us do in a week (Pontzer 2021, 2).

Using a fancy technique called the "doubly labeled water method," metabolism expert Pontzer and his research team measured how many calories the average hardworking, physically active Hadza person burned in a day. Surprisingly, they discovered the Hazda burn *the same number* of daily calories as you and me. How can this be? Given our comparatively sloth-like existence, how could we burn even close to the same amount of daily calories as a hunter-gatherer?

Pontzer discovered that people are allotted the same amount of energy each day, whether they spend that day running a marathon or sitting on the couch. Aside from some minor variations based on age and body size, everyone has the same "fixed energy budget." Says Pontzer, "The bottom line is that your daily activity level has almost no bearing on the number of calories you burn each day" (2021, 103).

On the surface, this doesn't make a whole lot of sense—until we look at the processes requiring energy *within* the body. We tend to think of using energy on things like exercise, running errands, and working, but it turns out there's a lot of calorie-burning happening behind the scenes as well: heartbeat, brain activity, digestion, and other essential organ functions we rely on to stay alive.

So, what happens if you don't exercise? Where does all that energy go that would otherwise get spent on weightlifting, walking, or Zumba? It turns out your body *must* use all its daily energy allotment. You can't just choose to spend a portion of it and save the rest for a rainy day. Much like sand in an hourglass, energy can't be stopped or removed from the body. You have to use it all within its twenty-four-hour circadian cycle.

Here's where being sedentary is problematic: Since your energy budget still needs to get used up even if you don't exercise or move, your body will put that energy to work on other things: inflammation, emotional rumination, stress reactions, even unruly cell division (a.k.a. cancer). Take a moment to let that sink in... After regular organ function, if you don't use your energy allowance for exercise and other movements, your body can use that leftover energy on unwanted processes—including overblown stress responses with their concomitant release of cortisol:

> Constrained daily energy expenditure changes the way we think about the role of exercise in our daily energy budget. With a fixed energy budget, everything is a trade-off. Instead of adding to the calories you burn each day, exercise will tend to reduce the energy spent on other activities. (Pontzer 2021, 239)

This explains how exercise mitigates stress (as well as depression, cardiovascular disease, and certain cancers). Exercise is good for you because it absorbs part of your daily energy quota so you don't have enough juice left for stressing. As Pontzer observes, "We have evolved to require daily exercise" (2021, 148).

2. Exercise Manipulates Hormones

Exercise also helps you expand your Settled Section. Through regular physical activity, you can become less sensitive to stress—meaning it will take a larger stressor to push you over the edge. This is because exercise affects the amygdala, the brain's fear center. Exercise lowers the amygdala's reactivity, modulating hormones released in the body (Kozlowska et al. 2015). Exercise also stimulates the release of feel-good hormones, including dopamine, adrenaline, endorphins, and endocannabinoids. This beautiful chemical soup helps stabilize our nervous system and improve resilience. Over time, exercise decreases cortisol and increases the proliferation of wellbeing-boosting growth factors within the brain. Notice I said "over time." In the short term, exercise actually increases stress hormones. But that is also helpful.

3. Exercise as a Stress Coach

It may seem a little counterintuitive, but another way exercise works its magic on stress is by causing stress. That's right: Exercise is a stressor. "Exercise, by definition, is the application of stress to our bodies," explains Dr. David A. Sinclair (Sinclair and LaPlante 2019, 103). You are physically stressing your body when you exercise, and your brain can't tell the difference between push-ups and a lion chasing you. To the brain, it's a job for the same hormones.

So, what's happening? How can exercise reduce stress when the mind sees it as a stressor? Think of exercise as graded stress exposure. Since exercise provides short, predictable, controllable stressors, it trains the body for longer, unpredictable, uncontrollable stressors. By introducing our bodies to cortisol-and-adrenaline release and recovery, the mild stress of exercise inoculates us against greater stresses.

Dr. John J. Ratey notes, "The paradox is that our wonderful ability to adapt and grow doesn't happen without stress." He points out that exercise "challenges the cells and create[s] waste products that can be just stressful enough" (Ratey and Hagerman 2008, 74). Physical activity redefines what is "too much to handle" and makes overwhelming stress seem more tolerable. That post-exercise glow isn't just the result of increased blood flow; it's as if the brain-body says to itself, "That wasn't so bad. We survived. We can handle this stress thing."

Cold exposure and intermittent fasting have a similar effect (in case you were wondering why taking ice baths and not eating before noon have become so popular). They too, as Sinclair points out, act as practice drills. The body considers these activities to be stressors since freezing or starving can threaten survival. So, they teach the body that it can overcome stress—just like exercise does.

How Exercise Causes Stress

Extreme exercise routines or exercising too frequently reverses the positive effects of exercise.

The recovery phase of a workout is just as important as the exercise itself. Without proper rest between periods of exertion, the body is more likely to misinterpret exercise as an actual threat (versus *training* for threat). When we over-exercise and don't rest enough, the brain-body doesn't feel like it can handle the workouts. The training effect is lost, and exercise becomes solely a stressor.

How do you know when you have crossed the line from healthful exercise to stressful exercise? Determining if exercise is excessive or overzealous is difficult because that point is different for everyone and can shift over time. It depends on your fitness level, stress sensitivity, and general health. Your workouts may have tipped the scale from helpful to harmful if you experience one or more of the following:

- Finding yourself unusually tired, despite getting enough sleep
- Becoming more prone to colds
- Getting injured frequently during exercise sessions
- Feeling irritable or lethargic an hour or two after a workout

These are signs of exercise burnout. If you're experiencing these symptoms, drop your workout intensity down 50 percent and include lots of time for rest and recovery. I recommend no more than two days in a row of exercise before having a rest day. You can always build (slowly) back to a more invigorating level later. Try tracking your exercise and record how you feel after various activities. In time, you will find your exercise sweet spot.

Being stuck in a stress state can also create exercise roadblocks. It's helpful to understand how this happens, especially since exercise helps move us *out* of a stress state. Let's take a look under the hood. Those excuses you make to avoid the gym might ultimately have some important unconscious, underlying causes.

First off, exercise improves your interoception, your soul speak. This is a good thing. But maybe there's a reason you've disconnected from your body. You probably dissociated out of self-protection (remember, freeze is a disconnection, but it also serves a purpose). When you come back into your body through exercise, it may feel like too much too fast. The reconnection can be overwhelming and scary. You might encounter resistance and wonder why you don't want to exercise again despite promising yourself that you would. In this case, your avoidance of exercise is trying to protect you.

For a lot of my patients, even a controlled physical activity feels remarkably like the uncontrollable stress they are trying to escape. Remember my client Jasmine from Chapter 9? After a traumatic breakup with her husband, she felt unhinged every time she started moving—whether it was officially exercising or just doing chores. Her brain was confusing the adrenaline release of a workout with that of an argument. This type of mismatch between movement and past stress is more common than we might think, and sensitivity to stress can easily translate into sensitivity to exercise.

When you're outside of the Settled Section and stuck in one of the extreme zones on the Stress Quadrant (fight-or-flight or freeze), the motivation to exercise seems out of reach. If you feel like you're being chased by a lion, you're too busy running away, defending yourself, or hiding to make exercise a priority. Focusing on exercise when your alarm system is in overdrive feels unrealistic. You're in survival mode, not fit-into-your-jeans mode.

Unfortunately, this is when we need exercise the most—when it seems unfeasible, unimportant, and unsafe. But in this state, adding exercise to your "shoulds" can be yet another stressor in itself and a source of what I call "self-care guilt." You start feeling like there must be something wrong with you since you can't commit to taking care of yourself. Personal trainers tap into this when they throw around mantras like "no excuses." These are meant to motivate clients, but they can backfire into shaming. Please remember your "excuses" may be stress responses. Stress has put you in a survival state, and your biology is now directing the show. Rather than shame it into submission, a more effective, gentle, and compassionate approach would be to settle your nervous system first. The following techniques will also help.

Making Exercise Your Friend

Regardless of your relationship with exercise or how much movement you can tolerate, there are ways to embrace physical activity and enhance its benefits.

1. Redefining Exercise

A good place to start is by changing our definition of exercise. Even the most mundane types of movement can be considered exercise.

In one of my favorite research studies, Dr. Alia Crum, who we met in Chapter 4, and Dr. Ellen Langer looked at the effect of mindset on the physical fitness of hotel cleaning staffs.

They gave the maids at seven hotels information on the benefits of exercise. At four of the hotels, they also informed them their housekeeping work satisfied government recommendations for staying active and told them how many calories they were burning during their most frequent tasks: changing bed linens, vacuuming, etc. The workers in these hotels became the "informed" group.

Subjects at the other three hotels were the "control" group. They received the same written description of the benefits of exercise, but they did not get information connecting those benefits to their physically demanding jobs.

After one month, the control group showed no health changes. The informed group, however, had lowered their blood pressure, lost an average of two pounds, and improved their body-fat percentages. Since there were no other changes in the subjects' exercise or nutrition, researchers attributed these results to a shift in mindset (Crum and Langer 2007).

This study points to the importance of our perception about daily exercise. All movement *is* exercise. It doesn't have to be big, intense, or fancy. We don't need gym memberships, complicated equipment, or huge time commitments. If you can't move as much as you would like, you can at least change your mindset so your regular activities—like cleaning, carrying groceries, walking to and from your parked car—help you harness the rewards of exercise.

2. Keep It Short and Sweet

Besides expanding your definition of exercise, you can move your body in gentle ways and for short durations. This takes advantage of the exercise-as-stress-trainer philosophy. Depending on your tolerance, this might mean feeding yourself exercise routines like you're feeding a baby bird—one little droplet at a time. Kasia Kozlowska and colleagues explain:

> Since, in the short term, exercise increases arousal (though the ultimate goal and result is to decrease arousal), some patients will need to start with forms of exercise, such as gentle yoga postures or other exercises with simple movements, that raise arousal in small increments. (Kozlowska et al. 2015)

Pacing yourself in this way also gives you time to adjust to the reconnection with your body that might be taking place.

3. Convey Safety

When exercising, it's also important to send cues of safety to the body. Doing so will augment the feel-good hormones associated with moving. Here are some helpful ways to do so:

- Move with friends—if you exercise with others, you're not only generating connection, camaraderie, and collaboration, you're also stimulating endorphins above and beyond those released during solo activities. Bonus points for synchronous movement, such as walking at the same pace or doing the same dance moves together.
- Move in nature to maximize the release of those feel-good hormones.
- Move to music. Rhythm speaks volumes to your calming nervous system.
- Play. If movement feels like stress to you, having fun should be the number-one emphasis. It's almost impossible to be playful while under threat (unless you're faking playfulness to distract or appease the threat). In general, play is associated

with being safe, so adding a sense of playfulness to your exercise tells your brain that all is well. You can use games, dance, children's activities, upbeat music, sensual sways, silly motions—whatever is fun for *you!*

- Engage your core. Strengthening the abdominal muscles (also called core work) boosts the calming effects of physical activity. There's a surprising connection between the brain's role in abdominal activation and the adrenals, which produce the stress hormone, cortisol (Drum, Levinthal, and Strick 2016). In an interview with the Atlantic neuroscientist Peter Strick, who helped make this discovery, says:

> There's all this evidence that core strengthening has an impact on stress. And when you see somebody that's depressed or stressed out, you notice changes in their posture. When you stand up straight, it has an effect on how you project yourself and how you feel. Well, lo and behold, core muscles have an impact on stress. (Hamblin 2016)

Gentle Movement Options

If more traditional exercise isn't possible for you right now, try some of the following movement options.

<u>Progressive Tension and Relaxation of the Body</u>

Start by lying comfortably on your back. Tense up your toes… then relax them. Work your way up your body—focusing on one muscle group at a time—squeezing and releasing, squeezing and releasing: toes, feet, legs, and so on, all the way up to the muscles in your face. If you Google "progressive muscle relaxation exercises," you will find many guided practice options.

Rag-Doll Shake

Start by standing, keeping a soft bend in your knees. Fold in half at your waist, arms hanging down toward the floor. Relax your neck. From this position, shake your arms then your legs (or both at the same time) for approximately thirty seconds before rolling up slowly… until standing upright again. If bending over towards your toes is difficult or painful for you, do the shaking from an upright position instead.

Core Work

Option 1

Weight Shift: If you can't tolerate sit-ups or planks, try simply shifting your weight back to your heels while standing. This automatically engages your core muscles, which, as I've mentioned, are associated with your calming nervous system.

Option 2

Laugh: One study found laughing can engage our core muscles as much as doing crunches (Wagner et al. 2014). If traditional core work isn't a viable option for you, try going to a comedy club, watching a funny movie, or spending time with some hilarious friends.

Option 3

Stork Stance: Balancing not only activates the core muscles, it also challenges the inner ear, which is linked to the pleasure centers in the brain (Todd and Lee 2015). Bend one leg and don't let it touch the other. Hold that single-leg stance for as long as you can—up to thirty seconds. When you're able to stand on one leg for half a minute without losing your balance, you can make this more challenging by *slowly* rotating your head from right to left while in stork stance.

Through the different theories on exercise, we can see how moving helps alleviate stress: It utilizes energy so little is left for stressing, provides stress in manageable doses as training for future stress, and manipulates the body's feel-good chemical messengers. Which theory resonates most with you? They all do for me! We don't have to pick just one; they overlap and can co-exist. The tools in this chapter use the knowledge of all three perspectives, guiding us as we find ways of making friends with exercise.

After you exercise, it's a good idea to stretch. If I'm wearing my physical therapist hat, I definitely recommend it. But does stretching help settle your nervous system? Does it help with stress? Let's find out.

CHAPTER 14

Stretch

Over the years I've treated a few patients who were absolutely obsessed with stretching. These clients usually fit a certain profile. Most often, they are striving, perfectionist women wearing many hats: homemaker, successful professional, supportive partner, doting daughter, driver of children, homework tutor, and best friend to many.

Eileen was one of those patients. She was hypervigilant in her approach to life—and her muscles played along accordingly. The need to relieve her physical and mental tightness led to incessant stretching, and eventually she started feeling unnecessarily guilty about her proclivity for releasing muscle tension. It was like an itch she always needed to scratch.

Eileen kept stretching bands and foam rollers (long tubes for rolling out tension) all over her house. Therapeutic balls, trigger point massagers, and other gadgets designed for kneading stiff body parts were the first items to go into her suitcase when she traveled. Her husband would tease her about all the stretching paraphernalia strewn about their house, but Eileen just couldn't get enough of the pleasurable, melting relief she got from lengthening and manipulating restricted tissues.

Rat Yoga

While researching the effects of stretching for *Move: How the New Science of Body Movement Can Set Your Mind Free,* Caroline Williams found herself in a laboratory at Harvard University watching a rat do yoga. It was holding the downward dog pose as part of Dr. Helene Langevin's studies on stretching. Using rats, Langevin observed how stretching decreases the inflammation triggered by chronic stress.

Stretching communicates safety to the immune system, waving the white flag and calling off the battle instigated by inflammation. Stretching, as Williams explains, "could act as a reset button that stops a bad day from turning into a runaway stress response" (2021, 154). For Eileen, stretching was her body's way of trying to recalibrate her nervous system. It was a cry for calm.

Limits on Being Limber

But don't wriggle into your yoga pants just yet, my friends. It turns out flexibility—like stress—has a Goldilocks zone. Both ends of the spectrum are associated with anxiety: either too much or too little fluidity in your joints, muscles, and fascia (strong connective tissue) can over-activate your stress response.

Only 20 percent of the general population has abnormally pliable connective tissue; however, Dr. Jessica Eccles, a researcher and psychologist, found that approximately 70 percent of people with anxiety disorders are also hypermobile. In brain imaging of hypermobile subjects, she and her colleagues found elevated activation in the amygdala, the brain's fear center. "We know," states Dr. Eccles, "that people with unusually flexible joints seem to have overly active fight or flight nervous systems" (Eccles 2017).

Eccles also found hypermobile subjects to have altered insulas—an area of the brain associated with representation of the body. It turns out that being super supple tends to distort our interoception. As fitness expert Jill Miller, who you met in Chapter 7, writes in the foreword to Libby Hinsley's *Yoga for Bendy People*, "Being hypermobile makes it very difficult to sense where your own body begins and ends" (Hinsley 2022, 62).

Miller would know; she's been living with the effects of rubber-like joints since age twelve, around the time she discovered she excelled at yoga. If your joints are especially yielding, you can perform with ease the most contorted yogic postures. This can lead to a sense of accomplishment and a desire to continue showing up at the yoga studio, but according to PT and yoga instructor Hinsley, doing yoga was "inadvertently exploiting" her hypermobility and ultimately exacerbating its problems (Hinsley 2022, 105).

What problems? If you're super bendy, at least you don't have to worry about stiff muscles, right? Actually, the opposite is true. When people have lax joints, the surrounding muscles overcompensate in an effort to provide stability, resulting in muscle spasms, tightness, and pain. Hyperflexiblity can lead to a stiff, sore body.

Flexible and Strong

Being too flexible and being too rigid are at opposite ends of a continuum, and either extreme can have negative repercussions. Similar to our Settled Section, a happy middle exists within the body's connective tissue matrix.

We see this in nature as well. Earthquakes are a good example. When I was fifteen, my family moved from Toronto, Canada to California, and earthquakes suddenly became a part of my life. I spent time crammed under a school desk waiting for the end of an earthquake drill while my father—a structural engineer—became interested in earthquake reinforcement and created a whole system to manage Mother Earth's version of a stress response.

Thirty years ago, the field of seismic retrofitting used steel "jackets" to prevent bridges and buildings from moving during earthquakes. My dad immediately saw that making something *more rigid* only made it more brittle and, therefore, more breakable. Taking a cue from nature, he gave buildings the ability to move—to sway—during an earthquake, like a tree in the wind. His new system allowed structures to be more flexible *and* more stable. By embracing the idea of being flexible yet strong, he created an entirely new way to keep us safe during earthquakes. (Yep! Proud daughter over here.)

We can look to our anatomy for hints on how this works in humans, too. Muscles are a symbol of strength; ask a four-year-old to show you how strong they are, and they'll flex their biceps for you. We equate tight muscles with strength. But a tight muscle is often a weak muscle. To contract optimally, it needs flexibility. If it isn't flexible, it doesn't function well, and the joint it protects and stabilizes becomes prone to stress and injury. Nearby muscles overcompensate and go into spasms. It's a downward spiral leading to pain—and maybe a visit to the doctor. Like a tree swaying in the wind or a building swaying in a quake, the body needs flexible strength.

How to Stretch

So where does this leave us with stretching? We know that being more flexible helps pacify the nervous system and protect the body from injury, but how do we know if we're overdoing it and causing harm? Whether double-jointed or stiff-jointed, the following suggestions will make sure your stretching routine is also a settling practice:

1. Use a curiosity mindset

Hinsley discovered a way to practice yoga while still protecting her super-flexible body—and those of her "bendy" patients—from the negative effects of hypermobility. She encourages using a "curiosity mindset" instead of striving for the perfect pose because "it's easy to get attached to external standards of what yoga postures are supposed to look like rather than what they feel like" (Hinsley 2022, 903).

Play detective in yoga or any stretching practice in which you are elongating tired, aching muscles. Ask the following questions to help keep your stretches soothing and safe:

- Am I feeling the stretch in the right place?
- Does this position feel safe, or am I panicking a little? You don't want your stretch to set off alarm bells. Check your breathing; does the position cause you to hold your breath or speed up your breathing?
- Am I feeling a diffused release, which would signify a good stretch? Or does the pull feel like a sharp, concentrated pain—a sign you've gone too far?

2. Slow down

Slowing the movements leading into a stretch helps keep you mindful and attentive as you investigate your body's feedback. Slowness also signals safety to the body.

When I taught massage to physical therapy students, I found a fun way of illustrating how connective tissue responds to pressure and stretching. I mixed corn starch and water into a putty-like substance. When you put your hands into a container of this concoction, different things happen depending on the pressure you use. If you move fast or apply too much force, the mixture fights back and you hit what feels like a solid block of cement. Slow down and let your hands rest lightly on the mixture, and your fingers sink into a soft, gooey substance all the way to the bottom of the container. The body likes to be stretched the same way: slow, steady, curious, and mindful. As Hinsley suggests, "Ask your body what it wants instead of telling it" (2022, 978).

3. Back away from the intensity

To stretch safely and effectively, you want to aim for as little as 30 to 50 percent of your full lengthening potential (Wyon, Felton, and Galloway 2009). Chances are you need to back off from how much you're pushing into your downward dog. Gentle stretching is effective stretching; you don't have to force it. A general rule of thumb is to back off of a full stretch by approximately 50 percent.

4. Hold for thirty seconds

Once you've found the right amount of stretch resistance, hold the position for a count of thirty seconds—studies suggest this is the optimal timespan for holding a stretch (Bandy, Irion, and Briggler 1997).

Note: If you believe you have hypermobility (which a good physical therapist can help you determine), then static stretching—stretches requiring you to hold a position at the end range—may feel good in the moment but backfires later. Instead, try dynamic mid-range stretching (e.g., lunges), where you move through a range of motion instead of holding a stretch. Self-massaging techniques and strength training can also be helpful. As Libby Hinsley shared with me in an email, "Getting the muscles stronger will help them relax, because in this case, it's the muscle strength that will help the nervous system feel settled."

5. Use expansive postures

Focus on movements that encourage the opening and expanding of your chest, particularly at the conclusion of your stretching routine. When we're overwhelmed, the need to protect ourselves kicks in, and we inwardly contract, causing the shoulders, head, and torso to droop. We collapse forward under the weight of any tension we're carrying. Consciously reversing that tendency helps send a message of safety to the mind. Remember, there's a bidirectional relationship between brain and body, so when we stretch in ways that open up the front of the body, we are communicating assurance and security to the brain. Skip this step, however, if chest expansion feels vulnerable to you. Remember, "It depends!" Play detective and listen to your body.

What to Stretch

Stretching any area of the body helps dial down stress, but the following stretches target muscles that, when tight, can constrict the vagus nerve or restrict breathing, either of which can negatively affect your ability to find your Settled Section:

Scalene Muscles Stretch

In Chapter 12, we discussed the importance of keeping neck muscles relaxed during inhalation. Remember the group of muscles called the scalenes? The ones on either side of the neck, running from the upper spine to the first two ribs? These are the muscles we tend to overwork, especially when we're in a constant state of fight-or-flight. Elongating these muscles can help move you away from hypervigilance and into a state of calm.

SCALENE MUSCLES

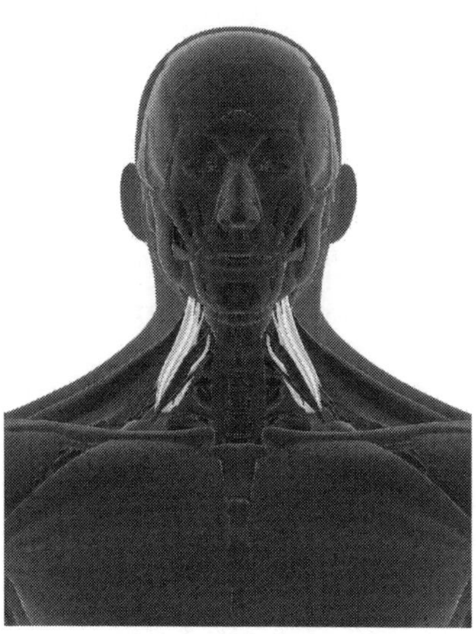

- To stretch the scalenes on the right side of your neck, bring your left ear towards your left shoulder. Maintaining this side-bent position, tilt your head up slightly so you're looking toward the ceiling.
- Remember you only need to go into 30 to 50 percent of your full stretch potential. Back off by approximately half of your full range of motion.
- Be sure to breathe from your lower ribcage and diaphragm as you hold that position for thirty seconds.
- Repeat the same stretch on the left side of your neck.
- Don't forget to pay attention to signs of downregulation or upregulation. How does your body respond to this stretch?

Psoas Self-Massage

Another muscle associated with breathing is the psoas (pronounced "soh-uhs"; strange name for a muscle, I know). From a Greek word meaning "muscles of the loin," the psoas is a hip flexor that connects the spine to the legs and allows you to bring your knee up towards your chest. It runs from the vertebrae in the low back, cuts diagonally through the body, and attaches to the inner thigh bone, the femur. Because of the position of this muscle in the body, people with tight (and exhausted) hip flexors often complain of lower back stiffness. The state of the psoas also affects breathing because these muscles intertwine with the ligaments and fascia of the diaphragm.

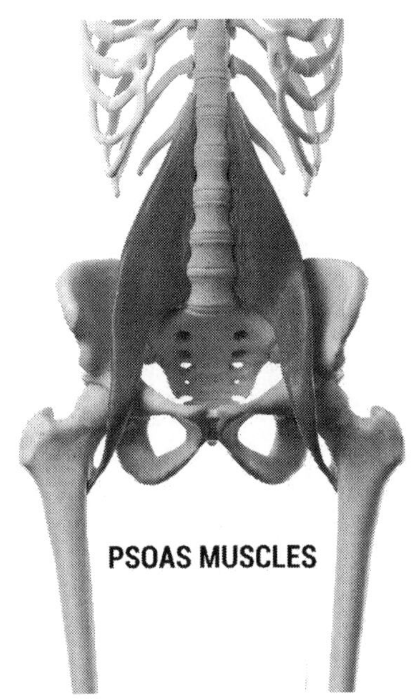

Liz Koch is what you might call a "psoas specialist." In *The Psoas Book* she writes, "People do not have 'weak' psoas muscles that need strengthening through standard muscle protocols, they have exhausted psoas muscles often due to an overwhelmed nervous system" (2012, 44). Williams, who witnessed the rats doing yoga, explains Koch's thinking nicely:

> Because of its position in the body, connecting breath with movement, the word on the street in yoga, Pilates and a dance-based combination of the two called gyrotonics is that the psoas is the muscle connecting the stress response to the physical act of running away and the extra-deep breaths that are needed to keep it up. And, since the psoas is shortened by too much sitting, the theory goes, it's hardly surprising that we are all so stressed: we are constantly in a state of half-formed fight-or-flight. (Williams 2021, 141)

There are many ways to stretch your hip flexors. One of my favorites is a self-release technique using a soft massage ball. (You can find information for purchasing massage balls in the Resources chapter.)

- To stretch your right psoas, place your right index finger on the front of your right pelvic bone, the bone below your waist that sticks out when you lie on your back.
- Place your left index finger on your belly button. Imagine a diagonal line between those two

fingers. The middle of this line is where to place your massage ball.

- If you want to make sure you're on the psoas muscle, gently bring your right knee up towards your chest. You should feel a muscle pop out in the center area of that diagonal line.
- Keeping the ball in that spot, lie face-down and relax over the ball. You can bend your right knee and turn it out so your inner thigh is resting on the floor, if that feels more comfortable to you.
- Stay in that relaxed position for a minute or two or until you feel a softening in the muscle. Aggressively pushing the muscle is counterproductive. This is a gentle self-massage.
- Repeat on the left side.
- As a reminder, you will find a QR code for the video of this technique in the very last chapter.

PSOAS BALL RELEASE

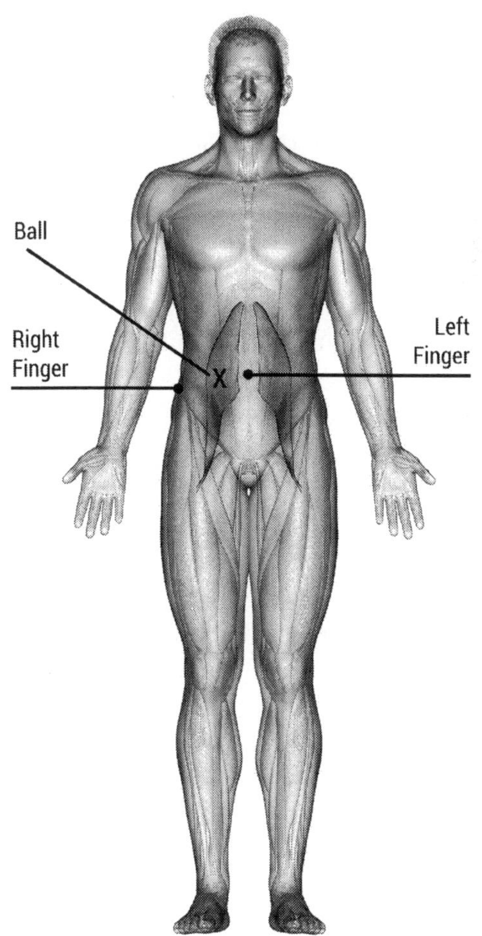

Sternocleidomastoid and Trapezius

In Chapter 2, we talked about "Vagus and The Quartet." The vagus nerve makes up 75 percent of your calming nervous system. The other 25 percent (the quartet) are neighboring cranial nerves, giving us easy access to the vagus and acting as portals to the calming nervous system.

Cranial Nerve XI is one of those nerves, and it feeds two muscles in the neck called the sternocleidomastoid (SCM for short) and the trapezius. Interestingly, of the 662 skeletal muscles in the body, the SCM and trapezius are the only two innervated by cranial nerves instead of spinal nerves. Perhaps this is why there is a strong correlation between neck pain and stress. A meta-analysis of twenty-eight different studies found that stress significantly increases your risk of neck pain (Ortego et al. 2016). Conversely, relaxation of these muscles can significantly relax the nervous system.

SCM Stretch

The SCM allows you to side-bend and rotate your head. When you turn your head to one side, the SCM is that tight band on the opposite side of your neck going from behind your ear down to your collarbone.

STERNOCLEIDOMASTOID

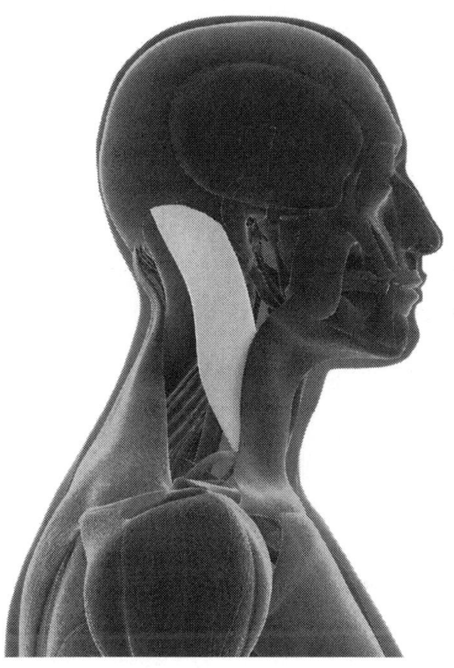

- To stretch your right SCM, bring your left ear towards your left shoulder.
- Maintain this side-bent position and rotate your head to the left, so you're looking towards your left shoulder.
- Maintain that position and tilt your head back slightly, looking up.
- Hold for thirty seconds, breathing slowly from your lower ribcage.
- Repeat on the right side for your left SCM.

Trapezius Stretch

The other muscle innervated by Cranial Nerve XI is the trapezius. There are three parts to the trapezius muscle, but the "upper traps" (the part that allows you to shrug your shoulders) is where we often hold a lot of stress. It's one of the first places I feel my stress. Tension in my neck and shoulders is a clue I need to settle my nervous system and do some stretching.

In a study looking at mental stress and trapezius muscle activation, researchers gave a group of "stressed" test subjects a supervised typing task involving mental arithmetic graded for miscalculations (yikes!). A group of "non-stressed" subjects was simply asked to type without supervision and without having to do calculations (much nicer!).

Researchers found that when stressed subjects were typing, their trapezius muscles became overworked, even though their posture hadn't changed. Oxygen monitoring revealed they also hyperventilated more than their non-stressed counterparts. This change in breathing was attributed to the exaggerated trapezius muscle activation (Schleifer et al. 2008).

TRAPEZIUS MUSCLES

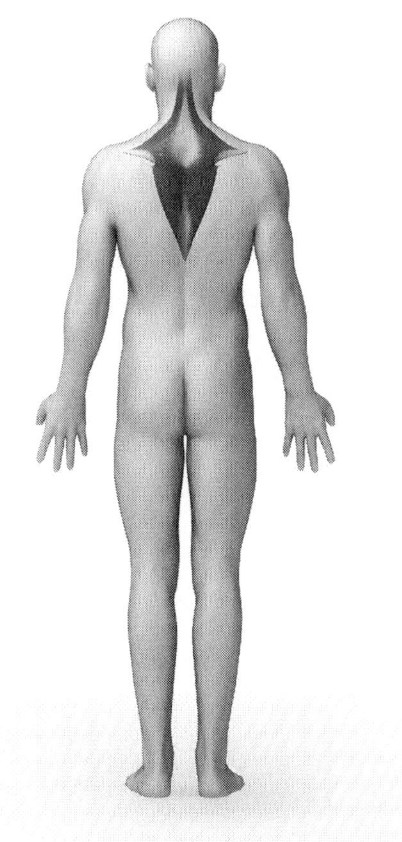

- To stretch the right-side upper trapezius, sit or stand up tall and place your right arm (elbow bent) behind you, resting it in the small of your back. This will anchor your arm for the stretch.

- Slowly bring your left ear towards your left shoulder without moving your body, only your head. Hold for thirty seconds.
- Repeat on the other side for the left upper trapezius.

I like to incorporate other settling techniques into my stretching routines. While holding these stretches, try doing a couple of physiological sighs (the double inhale, long exhale from Chapter 12). This will increase the effectiveness of your stretches.

Look for other ways to add or combine techniques and see what works for you. Just some food for thought. Speaking of food... The next chapter focuses on eating, and will give you even more practices for your self-regulation toolkit.

CHAPTER 15

Eat

When Marsha came to see me for her second session, she was ecstatic. "After only one week of practicing the tools, I've lost three pounds!" she exclaimed with a beaming smile.

I don't usually treat people for weight loss; I am not a dietitian or a nutritionist. Marsha—after a month of gaining five pounds per week—was looking for help regulating her nervous system because she attributed the jump on her scale to stress. And indeed, research on the relationship between stress, the gut, and weight is compelling.

The walls of the intestines contain a nervous system so important and complex that the gut is often called the "second brain." This brain in your bowels communicates with the brain in your skull through the "gut-brain axis," a pathway connecting your immune system, hormonal system, autonomic nervous system, and about 100 trillion microorganisms. I told you it was complex!

The communication between brain and gut goes both ways: Just as stress can cause digestive problems, gut inflammation can kick off a stress response.

What causes this kind of inflammation varies from person to person. Depending on your microbiome and personal tolerances, your gut may react to dairy, alcohol, sugar, gluten, or processed foods, just to name the biggies.

When I'm under stress, my digestion lets me know (I'll spare you the details!). The simple truth is we can't stress and digest at the same time. Digestion occurs when we are in a relaxed state. That's why the calming branch of the nervous system is called "rest and digest." So it doesn't really matter if we're following a paleo diet, a keto diet, or a cabbage soup diet—if sticking to it stresses out our brain, it stresses out our gut-brain too.

The reverse also happens: I can be without notable stressors, but if I'm indulging in too much sugar or alcohol (say, on vacation), I begin to feel irritable. The inflammation in my gut sends a message to my brain that something is wrong, and my brain interprets this message as emotional turmoil. This might be why I often get post-vacation blues. The bidirectional nature of the gut-brain axis means thoughts can affect our insides, and what we eat can affect our moods.

How Diets Create Stress

A sudden stressor usually causes sudden weight loss. Since stress mobilizes us into action, our drive to eat decreases while the body focuses on the crisis at hand. But when acute stress (like an accident) becomes chronic stress (like caring for an injured or ill family member), most of us tend to put on weight.

That is, unless our stress response causes nausea or compulsive calorie control. In general, when the source of stress is ongoing, the stress-weight correlation flips from decrease to increase. This is largely due to the overproduction of cortisol combined with coping strategies such as drinking alcohol, overeating, and zoning out in front of a screen.

I remember experiencing this shift during the COVID-19 pandemic. In the first weeks of lockdown, I lost weight. However, when it became clear the pandemic would persist, I started gaining weight. Admittedly, I was closer to my fridge and I had more time on my hands for mindless snacking. But it was the combination of my stress-related metabolism slump *and* my stress-related attempts to calm through food that really packed on the pounds.

After gaining my "COVID 15," I was tempted to seek out the latest weight-loss program. However, studies show diets actually increase weight in the long run (Tribole and Resch 2020). This is partially because diets often cause stress—and stress often causes weight gain. Now let's look at the ways diets create stress in the body.

First off, the very thought of needing to look slimmer—of needing to "correct" something about ourselves—causes anxiety. The self-loathing and self-criticism propagated by diet culture certainly do not come from a place of calm contentment. Anything that thrives on comparisons to others (e.g., perfectly photoshopped models) will generate a defensive stress response.

Moreover, when the metamorphosis we seek involves a grumbling stomach, the resulting starvation cue sends our bodies into survival mode. Hunger will naturally cause a stress response. Your body doesn't know you're purposely forcing yourself into a caloric deficit; it only recognizes the threat of starvation. Our survival instincts then urge us to raid the fridge.

Dieting requires hypervigilance. And that hypervigilance is another reason diets keep our alarm systems in survival mode. A study comparing dieters and non-dieters found the stress of chronic food restricting leads to biomarkers for decreased longevity (Blackburn and Epel 2017).

"Healthy" weight loss programs are not healthy if they put us in distress—the figurative weight of dieting can alter our ability to process nutrients properly. In one study demonstrating this, women were given either a breakfast consisting of healthy monounsaturated fats or a calorically identical breakfast consisting of unhealthy saturated fats. The results showed women with moderate-to-high stress had increased inflammation, regardless of the type of breakfast they ate. The positive effects of healthy fats were diminished by stress (Kiecolt-Glaser et al. 2014).

The stress of dieting isn't just physically harmful; it's damaging to our emotional wellbeing as well. Dr. Gary Bennett, a neuroscientist and psychology professor warns:

> One of the things we as a community need to talk more about is [that] all this effort that goes into trying to change our shapes exacts a toll on our emotions that may be riskier than the health consequences of obesity. (Godoy 2020)

How Stress Leads to Weight Gain

Being stuck in a stressed state leads to heightened levels of cortisol secretion, which causes the body to lay down more adipose tissue (i.e., fat) (Delker et al. 2021; Epel et al. 2000). When that stressor is a diet, not only do our nervous systems go into survival mode, but our fat cells do as well. Dr. Supatra Tovar, who we met in Chapter 12, is the creator of the online course "Deprogram Diet Culture" (see Resources section). She explains to me what happens when fat cells are stressed:

> During a diet, our bodies go into a starvation mode. The signals that come from our fat stores tell our bodies to slow down fat loss rather than speed it up. This is called "suppressed thermogenesis." Our bodies interpret dieting as starvation and therefore protect us against the deprivation. That protection comes in the form of resistance to utilizing fat stores and sluggish fat burning. This occurs during food restriction and after going off a diet.

Changes in Sugar Metabolism

Stress also causes insulin resistance, altering your ability to metabolize sugar. This explains why stress has been linked to Type II diabetes, a non-genetic, adult-onset form of the disease. Of course, not everyone under stress gets diabetes. In less severe cases, symptoms of insulin resistance include weight gain and insatiable hunger (Kyrou and Tsigos 2009).

Inflammation Nation

During acute stress, cortisol acts as an immune-enhancing, anti-inflammatory hormone. Over time, however, cortisol suppresses the immune system and becomes pro-inflammatory. That inflammation does two things:

1. It alters your gut microbiome, making it more difficult for you to digest and metabolize food.
2. It increases your chances of pain and injury because inflammation blocks nerve signals and proper muscle function.

Add the increased likelihood of getting sick due to a now-weakened immune system, and the combined effect will almost certainly derail your plans to finally use that gym membership. This is how increased cortisol from chronic stress reduces your motivation and ability to move your body. And, as we discussed in Chapter 13, being sedentary is fertile soil for stress. So around and around we go—on a vicious cycle of stress and weight gain.

Slumber's Side Effects

Sleeping less than seven and a half hours a night is also associated with weight gain. After sleep deprivation, your brain's endocannabinoid system becomes overactive. This means what it sounds like it means: the effects of insomnia mimic some of the effects of marijuana. The endocannabinoid system helps with sleep, memory, appetite, and other important functions. Excessive activation of this system—a consequence of poor sleep—leads to lethargy, decreased motivation, and an increased appetite for junk food (a.k.a. the munchies) (Hanlon et al. 2016).

Melatonin, a hormone produced by your pineal gland, increases in the evening hours to help you sleep, but melatonin decreases in the presence of too much cortisol. Essentially, stress dysregulates your melatonin, which disrupts your sleep, which decreases your energy to get moving, while stimulating your appetite for salty or sugary snacks. And here we are—caught in another vicious cycle.

Weighing in on Stress

Humans are inventive, and we adapt to stress in a variety of ways. To handle pressures that seem out of our control, we develop coping strategies—turning to behaviors that help us feel less of everything, including stress. We've discussed these numbing behaviors before. Food and alcohol are two of the most popular tools for numbing ourselves and dissociating from reality.

But we also use food for actual calming and soothing. Dr. Tovar has seen patients turn to favorite childhood comfort foods during times of stress. Eating does, in fact, shift our state to calm which is why we often feel sleepy after we eat. Caloric restriction (a.k.a. fasting), on the other hand, keeps us in a state of relative alertness.

The self-medicating effects of food are amplified with high-carbohydrate foods. I don't know about you, but I never hunger for broccoli when I'm feeling anxious. This makes biological sense: When we eat high-carbohydrate foods our bodies release serotonin, a feel-good hormone produced primarily in the intestinal tract. By releasing serotonin, that big bowl of pasta provides relief from the stress that made us crave it in the first place. Being on a diet takes away our comfort-food coping strategy *and* increases our stress, exacerbating our yearnings for the very foods we're trying to avoid. Hello again, vicious cycle!

Mindfulness Over Matter

Wanting to lose weight isn't wrong. We all want to look good in our favorite jeans, and studies show eating healthy and staying trim will lead to longer, better lives. But how do you navigate a weight-loss goal without eliciting a stress response?

Even if you stay away from restrictive diets, your relationship with food may still trigger stress. It's not like we can avoid food altogether! Then how do we take the stress out of eating so we can have the best possible chance of staying healthy? How do we break the vicious cycles?

I reached out to dietitian and nutritionist Michelle Babb for help answering those questions. Babb is the author of *Mastering Mindful Eating*, which reads like a guidebook on decoupling consumption from cortisol.

Babb describes mindful eating as "intentional eating" and recommends slowing down when we eat. The hurried, shoveling, multi-tasking approach to eating is sure to activate and perpetuate elevated fight-or-flight responses. If you consistently find yourself eating while driving or devouring a sandwich at your desk, try using Babb's fun, childlike technique for slowing down: Eat with your non-dominant hand. "It automatically switches you out of that autopilot response," she tells me.

She acknowledges that, given our harried culture, slowing down isn't always possible, but she advises connecting with our senses as much as we can when we eat. Perhaps you spend thirty seconds paying attention to your food's aroma or its texture as you chew. That simple shift can give your body "a small break from that stress response."

Stanford lecturer and executive coach Shirzad Chamine describes taking a similar approach with his clients: "When someone wants to lose weight, I don't coach them to go on any particular diet or eat any particular food. I go to the heart of the matter and ask them to commit to one thing: eating attentively" (2012, 152).

In the next chapter, we'll discuss in greater detail how to engage our senses. For now, here are some specific ways to incorporate mindful eating into your meals:

- Take in your food visually—notice the colors and shapes on your plate.

- Smell and enjoy the aroma of your food.
- Pay attention to the textures and temperatures of your food and notice if the flavors change as you chew.

"Treat eating like a sacred ritual," Babb suggests. A mealtime honored in an intentional way, "is much less likely to leave you wanting and craving," she says, "than eating as if you're in a fire drill" (Babb 2020, 19).

Whereas restrictive eating is stressful, a mindful approach takes stress out of your relationship with food. Over time, this "less stress, more pleasure" method of eating will naturally promote healthful food choices and provide an additional tool for your stress-management arsenal. Given the strong correlation between stress and weight gain, it's also a helpful tool for long-term weight loss, weight maintenance, and overall health.

As you approach eating from this angle, I would caution you to go slowly. If you've been using food to numb certain emotions, jumping full-force into mindful eating may bring up feelings of sadness, loneliness, or anger. These emotions are not "bad," but it's likely they're linked to valid reasons eating became a coping mechanism in the first place. When food is no longer suppressing these feelings, you may need support to process them. Please seek counseling assistance if necessary. Take your time. Go slow. Try little micro-moments of mindful eating until you build up a capacity to sit through an entire meal without the distraction of a book, newspaper, computer, phone, or television.

Stress-Reduction Instead of Dieting

Heart rate variability (HRV), a marker of overall health, refers to variations in time between successive heartbeats. Increased HRV (more variability) is associated with better functioning of the calming branch of the vagus nerve. Decreased HRV (less variability) is associated with increased risk of various health problems, including obesity.

Stanley Rosenberg, author of *Accessing the Healing Power of the Vagus Nerve*, suspects the association between obesity and low HRV holds a key to treatment for metabolic disorders and overeating. In his words, "I cannot help but speculate: What if their program for weight loss included evaluation of their HRV and improvement of their social engagement nervous system...?" (2017, 70).

I think Rosenberg is onto something. Turning your attention to reducing stress is a better approach than focusing on what you put (or don't put) into your mouth. After adding body-based regulation tools to her daily routine, my client Marsha lost weight—her daily practice of nervous system regulation carried over to the scale without her having to do much else.

To focus your efforts on taking stress off your plate, try using one of the following regulation tools before eating, or even before deciding what to eat:

Alternating Side-Eye

This tool is a variation on Rosenberg's technique called the "Basic Exercise" (2017, 186–190). You can do this while lying on your back, sitting down, or standing up. If you are lying down, bend your knees and place your feet flat on the floor. A pillow under your head is optional—whatever is most comfortable for you.

- Interlace your fingers. Place your hands behind your head at the base of your skull. The heels of your palms should rest against the bony areas right behind your ears.
- Keep your head in a neutral, straight position—not turned to the right or left. Move your eyes to look towards your left elbow. Hold your head still. Only your eyes move.
- Look in the direction of your left elbow for thirty seconds. If you experience a sign of down-regulation (sighing, yawning, tummy gurgling, etc.) prior to thirty seconds, this is your cue to move to the next position. If no sign of calming occurs, just keep holding the position for half a minute unless it's uncomfortable or up-regulating.
- After thirty seconds or a sign of down-regulation (whichever comes first), shift your gaze back to center. Hold it there for a couple of seconds.
- Now, move your eyes to look towards your right elbow, keeping your head still. Hold for thirty seconds or until you feel a sign of nervous-system relaxation.

The side-to-side eye movements in this exercise are akin to techniques used in an emerging field of psychotherapy called eye-movement desensitization and reprocessing (EMDR) therapy.

Created by Dr. Francine Shapiro, this treatment uses eye movements to suppress the brain's fear centers, providing relief from traumatic memories. By targeting the fear circuitry in the brain (specifically in the amygdala), EMDR reduces anxiety and relaxes the threat reflexes that trigger stress responses. In other words, moving our eyes from side to side can have a calming effect (Baek et al. 2019).

Jaw Release

One of my favorite ways of settling my nervous system before sitting down to eat is to release my jaw. Every part of the body has a story to tell, but the jaw tends to hold onto intense feelings and stress. Clenching the jaw restricts the natural processing of anxiety and hurt. It also compresses the temporomandibular joint (TMJ), limiting blood circulation in the trigeminal nerve. As you may recall from Chapter 2, this cranial nerve is linked to the vagus, making it a gateway into your calming nervous system. Releasing a tight TMJ helps improve vagal tone, in turn providing an overall settling effect.

Because the jaw is so intimately involved in eating, this technique works well for me as part of a calmer approach to consuming food:

- Lightly place your fingertips on either side of your jaw, just in front your ears. Open and close your mouth a few times. You will feel movement under your hands if you are in the correct position.

- Let your tongue rest on the roof of your closed mouth.
- With your fingertips on each side, slowly massage your jaw, using a gentle, circular motion.
- After four or five little circles, glide your hands down slightly following the jawline and massage there for a while.
- Continue rubbing in a circular motion as you follow along your jawbone until you reach your chin.

You can repeat this process a few times if you like. You do not need a lot of pressure. A light touch is a powerful way to communicate with your nervous system. Anything too forceful will set off a threat response—the exact opposite of our goal in this exercise. Let your hands be a messenger of safety and caring.

For a more advanced version, jut your lower jaw forward *slightly* as you perform this self-massage. Try it first without the change in jaw position. If that feels comfortable, try shifting the lower jaw forward, checking in with your body to see if this position proves helpful. Whichever position you're using, don't forget to look for signs of calming. Play detective!

Settle then Savor

Settling (using these exercises) and savoring (through mindful eating) are the two key approaches to food that will quell what *Intuitive Eating* authors Evelyn Tribole and Elyse Resch call that "chronic background anxiety that looms with every food choice" (2012, 33).

Through settling and savoring, we can break the vicious cycle of stress and weight gain and dig in to a more fruitful relationship with food. (Yes, those puns were intended. Sorry!)

Now that you've used your senses to reset your relationship with food, let's discuss how to use the senses to reset your nervous system—to find your way and help you stay in the Settled Section.

CHAPTER 16

Sense

"Stop. Be *here*! See *now*!"

This is what I say to myself when I'm feeling overwhelmed or restless. If my internal world becomes too uncomfortable, I anchor myself in the external world using my senses.

Of the five senses—touch, taste, smell, sight, and hearing—most of us have one or two that we gravitate towards. For me, it's my auditory sense. This may seem surprising, given that I was born with a hearing impairment and wear hearing aids in both ears. But when I use my sense of hearing to consciously take in the kids playing next door, the rustling of leaves, or the ticking of a clock, I feel my body lighten slightly. When auditory input is clear, it helps me feel safer. Perhaps this is why hearing is my favorite sense in spite of my disability.

My client Raven discovered her sensory preferences at a young age. She learned that tuning in to her sense of touch helped her feel grounded and safe during times of upheaval.

Raven was born with a rare illness that twisted her bones into knotted spirals. When she was sixteen, she was admitted to Children's Hospital Los Angeles to have metal rods inserted into her thigh bones. During the procedure, her right hip fractured. What was supposed to be a four-hour surgery turned into an eleven-hour nightmare.

Raven remembers how cold and sterile the hospital room was during her long recovery. "Hospitals have come a long way since the green, gray, and white walls," she says. "I was there for almost two months. My mom and my auntie tried everything to make me feel at home. They hung pictures on the walls, snuck in homemade food..."

She wanted them to bring in her down comforter since she particularly hated the "starchy, hard" hospital bedsheets. But the drainage apparatus attached to her leg was messy, and the comforter difficult to clean. She recalls, "Nothing really helped until they bought me some petal-pink sheets—the color of rose quartz—and a squishy pillow I could mold and hug to my chest. It was so much better than those white sheets with the one blue stripe down the center."

Raven remembers pulling her new, pink sheets up over the hospital-issued "scratchy white blanket" to make it more bearable—to make everything more bearable. She'd run the soft sheets back and forth between her fingers, attempting to ignore her excruciating pain. "Most of the nurses were kind and caring. One nurse—for whatever reason—it pissed her off," Raven tells me. "She called me a princess."

Raven also listened to her "yellow, sporty Walkman." She liked the soundtrack of the movie *Boomerang* and the mixed tapes her friends brought on their visits. "The music and the feel of the sheets would soften me," Raven recalls. The callous nurse had no power over her then.

As time passed, Raven continued to pay particular attention to the way fabrics felt to the touch. "If I dated someone who wore a lot of polyester," she says, "it didn't feel safe to hug them." Now in her forties, Raven is married to a man who wears only natural fibers and says, "It's soothing to be in his arms."

What Is Your Sensory Superpower?

Raven found she was "picky" about textiles. From my perspective, touch and hearing were her superpowers. In her otherwise bleak hospital room, Raven could cradle herself in the sensations of soft sheets on her skin and music in her ears.

Being mindful of sensory input sends cues of safety to the nervous system. Bringing attention to what you see, hear, feel, smell, or taste tethers you to the present moment, calming the nervous system and soothing the mind. Your senses welcome you to a more settled state—you "come to your senses."

When we are settled, our senses blossom; the world seems more vibrant: the flowers look brighter, the birds sound sweeter, the barbecue smells more delicious. (Ever wonder why food tastes better when you're on a relaxing vacation?)

Learning to Fly

Try focusing on a different sense each day for five consecutive days.

As you go about your usual activities, be cognizant of the "sense of the day." Take inventory of the ways a sense helps you—or doesn't help you—feel more supported and regulated. This exercise will heighten your appreciation of your senses, help you determine your preferences, and give you practice incorporating your sensory superpowers into your life.

Vision:

Focus on the objects, colors, and light patterns around you.

Try not to pass judgment on what you are seeing. If the sight of dirty dishes on your kitchen counter has you clenching your jaw and tensing your belly, try to let go of that analysis and just see. Change your optics. If that seems like an impossible Jedi mind trick, try noticing instead the way light creates shadows in the kitchen or the different hues within the space.

Bonus Exercises:

Orienting

As you look around, *slowly* turn your head to the left and right. This activates Cranial Nerve XI.

You may recall from the chapter on stretching that this nerve is part of the social engagement system. It interconnects with the vagus nerve, providing a gateway to the calming Stillness System, and it innervates the sternocleidomastoid muscle which allows you to turn and tilt your head as you look around.

Turning your head back and forth in this way enhances the potency of attuning to your visual field and helps you connect to a peaceful serenity.

Panoramic Vision

When we are in the upper limits of the Movement System (i.e., jazz hands!), our visual sense narrows into a type of tunnel vision.

In an interview for *Scientific American*, Stanford neuroscientist and professor of ophthalmology Dr. Andrew Huberman explains what happens to your eyesight when you're in a state of fight-or-flight: "Your visual system goes into the equivalent of portrait mode on a smartphone. Your field of vision narrows. You see one thing in sharper relief, and everything else becomes blurry" (Wapner 2020).

By causing our eyes to do the opposite of this evolutionary mechanism, we open our sense of sight into what Huberman calls "panoramic vision, or optic flow." This tells the body you are safe and able to take in a wider, broader view of the world around you.

This may explain why watching a sunset or sunrise can feel so calming—not only are you receiving the benefits of Mother Nature's beauty, but by taking in the horizon and everything in your periphery, you are engaging in panoramic vision, which "releases a mechanism in the brainstem involved in vigilance and arousal" (Wapner 2020).

Panoramic vision can be practiced anywhere, any time:

- Without moving your head or eyes, take in as much of your *distant* visual field—above, below, and to the sides—as possible.
- Feel your eyes soften, almost as if they are relaxing farther back into your skull.

This type of optical exercise is particularly calming when you are in nature, but it works well in any setting. I use it when I feel myself getting tense while working at a computer. Gaze over the top of the computer screen and take in as much as possible. Can you feel your breathing change? Any shift in tension in your shoulders, neck, or jaw?

Hearing:

Tune into sounds in your environment. Become more aware of the noises around you—the faucet dripping, the dog's collar announcing her whereabouts, the dryer tumbling clothes. Listen to sounds outside—the birds, the squirrels, leaves blowing in the wind. Maybe try using a sound machine (there are apps for this) and see if it helps you settle.

Try listening to various kinds of music, with and without vocals. Listen to chimes. Don't forget to listen to the silence. Tuning into the spaces between sounds can be just as effective as focusing on the sounds themselves.

Bonus Exercise:

Phone a Friend

Another nerve that is part of the quartet making up the social engagement system is the facial nerve (a.k.a. Cranial Nerve VII). It innervates the stapedius muscle of the middle ear, which allows us to hear sound frequencies specific to human speech.

Active listening can stimulate this nerve, providing a portal to your calming nervous system. Instead of texting a friend, try calling or having a video conference. The sound of a friendly human voice can go a long way toward helping your nervous system land in a relaxed state.

Smell:

Certain smells we encounter daily don't always register with our conscious brains. When you focus on olfactory input, those smells become more striking. This input may activate vivid memories, but for this exploration, try to just notice the fragrances in your environment without judging them as good or bad.

Take in the smells of foods, perfumes, fresh-cut grass, the permanent marker you're writing with. Light a scented candle. Try smelling anything and everything you pick up. People will think you are weird, but only for one day. It's all for the sake of science and figuring out your superpower.

Touch:

Your skin is the largest organ in your body. Yep, skin is an organ. Having been a massage therapist at the start of my career, I have a deep respect for the magic of healthy, appropriate touch.

When you begin your tactile exploration, start by noticing the feel of your clothes on your body. Get a clearer sense of what the fabrics feel like on your skin and the relative tightness or looseness of your outfit. Then become aware of any other surfaces you're in physical contact with. What are you sitting on? (Or lying on? Or standing on?) Are you resting your arms or hands or feet on anything? Are the surfaces you're touching hard or soft? Rigid or forgiving? Rough or smooth? Do you feel itchy? What temperature are you feeling?

As you go through your day, pay attention to any tactile stimulation you might experience: water on your body from the shower, a brush going through your hair, the feel of clean dishes as you put them away, your pet iguana's skin as you play with her. (You do have one of those, don't you?)

Next, try some self-touch techniques. Bring your hands together and give yourself a hand massage for a couple of minutes. Connect to how that makes you feel. Sweep or tap both hands from the tops of your thighs down to your knees. Repeat three to five times, trying different pressures, firm or light. What resonates best with you?

Bonus Exercises:

Plantar Fascia Foot Rolling

Place a small ball (a tennis ball with a folded towel covering it works well) on the floor and rest your foot on it. This can be done seated or standing. Roll the ball around the arch of your foot, moving slowly towards your toes. Spend a couple of minutes experimenting with what kind of pressure feels best to you.

With this exercise you are releasing your plantar fascia, which is a sheath of connective tissue protecting the bottom of the foot. The plantar fascia interdigitates with the calf muscles at the back of the lower leg, and continues up the chain to the hamstrings along the back of the thigh.

The back of the body is associated with a flight stress response (Johnson 2021). Releasing the plantar fascia allows for a "letting go" of the muscles in the back of the leg, resulting in a grounded feeling.

You are releasing your trapped urge to run away from life and digging into a sense of safe arrival.

SCM Massaging

We discussed the sternocleidomastoid, or SCM, in Chapter 14 and learned how to stretch this muscle. You can also massage the SCM. This is another self-massage technique that can be done either sitting or standing:

- Rotate your head to the left. On the right side of the neck, the muscle will pop out. It is a tight band running from just behind the ear and forking out in two branches to the sternum and collarbone.
- Using a light touch, place your fingers just behind the base of your ears.
- Gently sweep them straight down along the tight band-like muscle on the right.
- Follow that band down to your right collarbone, closest to your throat.
- Repeat five to ten times, sweeping from behind the ear to the upper shelf of the sternum and collarbone.
- Pay attention to how that massage technique registers in your body.
- Repeat on the left side of the neck.

STERNOCLEIDOMASTOID

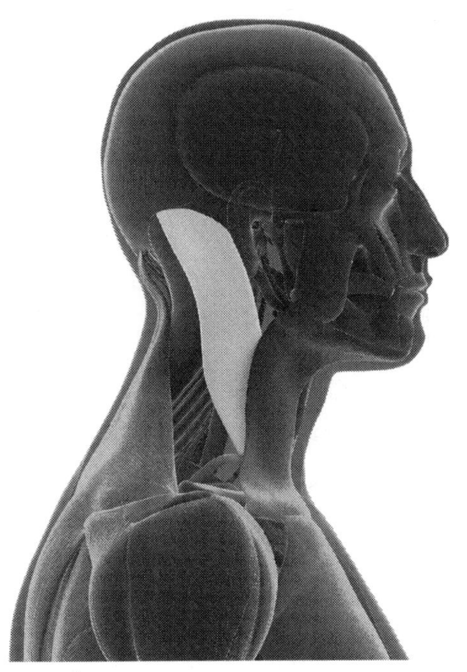

Note: You can also choose to gently pinch the SCM to release it. When you turn your head, use your thumb and index fingers to softly pinch the band-like muscle from just below the ear down to the collarbone. Remember to check out the video of this technique at the link found in the concluding chapter.

Taste:

As I mentioned in Chapter 15, slowing down and engaging with our senses while eating can improve our relationship with food.

On the day dedicated to your gustatory input, I suggest avoiding all screens and reading materials while you eat. No watching TV, responding to emails, or reading the newspaper during meals or snacks on this day. I know! Super difficult to accomplish. I am with you.

Instead, focus on the flavor of your food, one bite at a time. Put down your utensil in between each mouthful. Savor one morsel before moving on to the next. Closing your eyes while you chew may help with this. What is that spice? Can you tell if it is the texture or the taste of your food impressing your palate?

Tracking Your Flight Path

You may want to set a few reminders on your phone for a sense of the day check-in. These reminders can be every hour on the hour or several times a day at random increments. It is totally up to you.

At the end of the day, jot down how it felt for you to connect with the given sense. Did you feel a greater "sense" of calm afterwards? If so, how did you know? Did you feel more irritated? Or was there no noticeable change? If you did experience a shift up or down in your state, how long did it last?

At the end of the five-day experiment, pick the one or two senses that helped you the most. Ta-da! You now have your sensory superpower. It is time to fly! The fancy action-hero cape is optional (but highly recommended!).

Sensory Sensitivities

Be careful not to push yourself too much while experimenting with your senses. These exercises are meant to be enlightening, enlivening, and comforting. Please do not feel compelled to poke and probe into an area that doesn't sit well with you. Maybe you have a strong aversion to certain smells, sounds, or other inputs.

Sensory sensitivity may occur due to trauma, autism, hypervigilance, attention deficit hyperactivity disorder (ADHD), or as a reaction to stress. Sometimes this can be empowering—as was the case with Raven and her tactile sensitivity. Other times, it can evoke a stress response, which—in this case—is not our goal.

For example, it can be challenging for people with olfactory sensitivity to share an elevator with someone wearing cologne. Hyperosmia is a heightened sense of smell that may be genetic or acquired, and osmophobia is an aversion to smells often associated with migraines. When I am working with patients, I make sure not to wear any perfume because these olfactory sensitivities tend to be fairly common.

Intense negative emotions to specific sounds is called misophonia. People with this condition may be triggered into a stress response (usually fight-or-flight) by repetitive clicking sounds such as gum chewing, water dripping, or fingers tapping on a keyboard.

Tactile defensiveness is a sensitivity to touch. This can present itself as an aversion to seams on clothing, hugging, and, in particular, light touch. For some, a firm handshake versus a light handshake is more than just a preference—it is a sensory orientation.

Managing Sensitivities in an Overly Stimulating World

"Neurodiversity" refers to variations in learning, socializing, or mood processing. Examples of neurodivergent folks include those with autism, ADHD, dyslexia, and bipolar disorder.

Janae Elisabeth discovered her autism at age twenty-nine.

"I see sensory sensitivity as kind of a defining factor of neurodivergence," she tells me during an online interview.

> I was always a person who would seek out soft things before I knew I was autistic... I like really soft, soft things and cozy environments. And then I found out that my nervous system actually needs these things. My body system was pretty wise about that.

To others with sensory sensitivities, Janae advises:

> Sensory sensitivity can be really difficult because our world is so antagonistic to our sensitivity. And it can also be really wonderful and beautiful and a gift in many ways. I would advise people to ignore the stigma as much as possible—tune out what people are saying about people who are sensitive.

To Janae, sound can be both intolerable and calming, depending on the situation. Unnatural sounds—a lawnmower, for example—are like sandpaper on her nervous system. In contrast, she often finds the melodic predictability of old-school country music to be soothing.

Her sense of vision, too, is both a superpower and a source of overstimulation. "I have a low visual threshold," she shares, adding:

> Clutter can easily overwhelm me. And so, I start to kind of disconnect and dissociate because there's just too much visual noise. I like to compensate for that by keeping an organized space and having places for everything—or at least containers for everything. But by the same principle, because it's a low threshold, it only takes a little bit of positive visual imagery to positively impact me as well. This weekend I went out into the woods for about two and a half hours. It is peak fall season right now. The colors are just gorgeous. Just being able to look at the trees for a little while, I could feel my nervous system resetting and starting to downregulate...

As we have seen with both Raven's and Janae's sensitivities, the same type of stimulation can be both empowering and unbearable. Finding ways to shift your sensory sensitivity from a burden to a superpower is a matter of trial and error.

Now, Janae guides others through that process as a professional neurodiversity advocate known as the "Trauma Geek." (See the Resources section.)

According to Janae, there are two contrasting ways of handling sensory overload:

1. Avoid

You protect yourself by blocking the incoming sensory stimulation. This might include taking more breaks when working or wearing earmuffs ("ear defenders") to reduce noise. The other strategy is to shift to a different sensory stimulation. For example, using a fidget toy to help cope with noise intolerance.

2. Seek

Janae suggests "creating some intention around avoiding the things that are overwhelming and seeking out the things that have been really grounding and safe." She recommends creating a "sensory menu"—a list of activities that are calming. When we become overstimulated, "we tend to forget or have some brain fog come along with the overwhelm." A sensory menu provides a visual reminder of where to go for support when we might otherwise not be able to think clearly.

Her personal menu currently includes having tea, taking a nap, walking outside, taking a hot shower, dancing, doing yoga, and journaling. These are the activities Janae turns to when she feels overstimulated and wants to settle.

Next Up

We have looked at how changing our breathing, moving and stretching our bodies, feeding ourselves, and sensing our environment can cultivate stability in the Settled Section.

These tools and resources can help you regulate yourself as you make your way through life. They work on an individual level and don't require the participation of others for success.

But we are social beings. How do our connections with others affect our place on the Stress Quadrant?

That is the topic of the next four chapters.

Step Seven:

Connect with Others

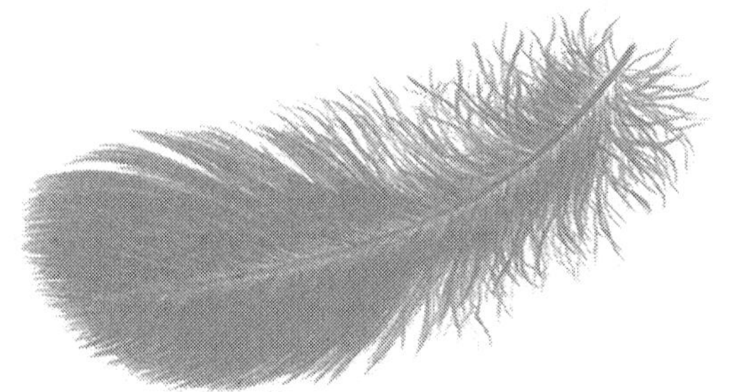

CHAPTER 17

Our Connection to Connections

Humans are social beings. Tribal networks are the cornerstone of our survival.

I have long understood the power of a loyal group of friends, but when my tribe of girlfriends took me on a beach getaway for my fiftieth birthday, it led to a level of social connectedness that changed my life.

The birthday trip was filled with laughter, gourmet cuisine, walks on the beach, and late-night conversations that peeled back the onion layers of superficial discourse. However, a few days after returning home, the ennui of everyday life began to dampen the soul-flutters we'd felt at the beach.

Then Emily sent Jill and me a text, saying, "We all seem to have something we need help with in our lives. What if we bonded together to help each other? What if we connected on a regular basis and recreated the uplifting feeling of our weekend getaway with purpose and consistency?"

The three of us met that day. How three busy moms were able to find two hours for an impromptu meeting is still a mystery to me. The stars aligned, and so did our schedules.

Sitting on my back patio with Cobb salads from a local restaurant, we brainstormed a plan that still bolsters our lives years later: We would become one another's confidantes, coaches, cheerleaders, and amateur therapists (recommending real therapy, of course, if necessary). We even gave our trio a name—Operation Springtime.

The name seemed fitting since we started with some "spring cleaning" and reorganizing of our lives and formed our group during a time of chirping birds and fresh garden blooms. To this day, we continue to help each other Marie Kondo our messy, cluttered lives—curating what brings us joy and giving away the rest. We are three women squeezing every drop of benefit out of our human connection. It is a powerful, magical union.

Co-regulation

Human connections provide co-regulation. Co-regulation occurs when we feel safe and align ourselves with another person's regulated nervous system. When these relationships work, they work wonders. During an amicable exchange with a friend's socially engaged nervous system, we become more modulated, attuned, and stable.

Just days before her birthday, author Anne Lamott reflected on the importance of solid friendships:

> By 68, you know that the whole system of our lives works because we are not all nuts on the same day. You call someone and tell them that you hate everyone and all of life, and they will

> be glad you called. They felt that way three days ago and you helped them pull out of it by making them laugh and a cup of tea. (2022)

What Lamott is talking about is co-regulation. It can save us from the stress in the world—and in ourselves.

Wired for Connection

Biology knows how important attachment is for human survival. Our anatomy has made the connection—literally. As our vagus nerve evolved, it became physically linked to the cranial nerves that help us communicate with one another. Social connection is hardwired into being human. We evolved to need attachment.

"We come into the world wired for connection, one autonomic nervous system reaching out to another," says social worker and Polyvagal Theory expert Deb Dana. That drive for social connection is a "biological imperative," she states, "essential for survival" (Dana 2020, 170).

The vagus nerve and the communication-oriented cranial nerves (recall, if you will, "Vagus and The Quartet") combine to form our social engagement system. Our vocal tones, facial expressions, head gestures, eye contact—these are all vehicles into the nervous system's calming mechanism. These face-to-face connections provide portals to that feel-good, sustainable stillness.

It is not surprising that human connections promote physical health, build emotional support, foster resource sharing, encourage task division, and offer protection. In her TED Talk on social connection, psychologist Susan Pinker outlines the top-ten predictors of longevity. Number one? Being social. Number two? Also being social. The practice of having daily casual interactions with others—even strangers—and maintaining an abundance of close relationships does more to increase longevity than keeping trim, getting flu shots, or quitting smoking (Pinker 2017).

Loneliness, on the other hand, wreaks havoc on one's health. As journalist John Leland reports in the *New York Times*: Social isolation is associated with an additional $6.7 billion in Medicare spending and costs employers more than $154 billion annually in stress-related absenteeism and job turnover (Leland 2022).

He found the growing health consequences of loneliness are "driven by the accelerated pace of life and the spread of technology into all of our social interactions" (Leland 2022). The more connected we are on the internet, the less connected we are in the break room, locker room, and family room.

Connections help us when we get to that fork in the road. They escort us away from the "stress will hurt you" path and onto the "stress will help you" trail. On our journey, solid relationships can keep those adverse childhood and epigenetic factors from leading us astray. In fact, according to Dr. Bruce D. Perry, "Connectedness has the power to counterbalance adversity" (Perry and Winfrey 2021, 108).

Whether we are extroverted or introverted, easily agitated or inspired in social settings, we all need some form of connection with others. Some of us need more alone time, others more commingling, but—regardless of our preferred quantity, frequency, and duration—we are all designed to connect.

Sisters Emily and Amelia Nagoski explain the crucial back-and-forth between alone time and relational time: "Connection—with friends, family, pets, the divine, etc.—is as necessary as food and water. Humans are not built to function autonomously; we are built to oscillate from connection to autonomy and back again" (2019, 152).

High-Frequency Friendships

Don't let my sunshiny description of Operation Springtime mislead you. My focused time with Emily and Jill isn't always rosy repartee and air kisses. We've had many difficult conversations. We push each other into uncomfortable places. We are accountability buddies, truth-tellers, bullshit detectors, screaming boards, frustration balls for squeezing, and shoulders to cry on. Our meetings are not just social events; they are work. Our time together can be raw, vulnerable, ugly, sweet, enlightening, scary, tender, and enlivening all at once. We have leveled-up our friendship in such a way that it transforms the bond itself while continuing to transform us.

In *How We Show Up*, Mia Birdsong writes about a similar circle of friends:

> [My group] is an alchemy, whereby we create more love and time and energy together than we hold individually. At our best, we don't

> function based on reciprocation. It's not about getting as much out of it as we put in. It's that our output is transformed into a wholly different material that's not possible to create alone. (Birdsong 2020)

That is what happens with Operation Springtime: As a group, we become something that isn't possible alone. I call these higher vibrational connections "high-frequency friendships." They don't happen automatically. You have to take action and will them into existence through consistency and determination.

I have two other high-frequency friendships (HFFs). The first one started as an online Sunday women's book club and morphed into what we now affectionately call "The Church Ladies Group." We don't discuss books anymore; we often veered from the book's topic anyway and found our tangential discussions more rousing. Now we check in with one another and offer support. Our cohesion creates trust wherein meaningful dialogue happens. Despite no religious affiliation, my time with the Church Ladies is nothing short of a spiritual tonic for my heart and soul.

My other HFF comes from daily check-ins with my friend Deanna. She and I borrowed the idea from modern feminist Regena Thomashauer (a.k.a. Mama Gena), who outlines three truths to share with a friend "on the daily." Thomashauer calls them the "holy trinity," and they help us stay in touch with our "natural radiance" (2016, 176–177).

Every day, Deanna and I text each other (1) something we are proud of, (2) something we are grateful for, and (3) something we desire. We refer to these as our daily BGDs (brag, gratitude, desire). They help us focus our days, support each other, and celebrate our strengths, successes, blessings, and wants.

Our routine also helps us catch stress patterns. For example, if a genuine boast won't materialize organically and takes effort for two or three days in a row, that's a red flag. I see it as a sign that I am not emotionally grounded; I need to use more self-regulating tools, pamper myself, and practice self-compassion. BGDs not only foster high-frequency friendships but also help us gauge fluctuations in our wellbeing.

This isn't just for women. Men benefit from HFFs as well. When my son was in elementary school, my husband and some of his friends formed a group called the DUDES—an acronym for "Dads Uniting Dads in Education and Service." Combining their sense of camaraderie with their desire to serve the community, the DUDES host school fundraisers, fix worn-out sandboxes, set up chairs for assemblies, march with their kids in the local Fourth of July parade, and even jump school fences after hours to paint peeling classrooms. (Yes, that really happened, *and* they wore camouflage!)

The DUDES grew right along with their kids. The group now includes fathers from other elementary schools, the middle school, and the high school. They do engage in the occasional sports competition and consume the occasional beer (this is a dads club after all!). But as my husband will tell you, behind the scaffolding of these activities is a structure built on purpose, mutual respect, and fun. As he puts it, "We're creating friendships that are deeper and more meaningful than simply socializing."

How to Create High-Frequency Friendships

1. Find a quiet place, preferably in nature, where you can be alone. Somewhere you feel safe and serene. Think about your friends and acquaintances. Who makes you feel relaxed—shoulders drop, jaw unclenches, heart rate slows? Who leaves you feeling energized instead of depleted? "The purpose of our closest relationships is to build energy," says psychologist Dr. Lindsay Gibson. "Using this energy barometer is a foolproof method for recognizing people you need to be with" (2020, 244). Find your vibrancy boosters. Write their names down on a piece of paper or in a journal.
2. Reach out to the people on your list. The creation of HFFs takes active participation on your part. Send some emails or texts (heck, you could even *call*). Put suggestions out into the ether. Be specific about what you are looking to create. Remember, this isn't about superficial networking; the mission is meaningful connection.
3. Set down some gentle rules. Support is the goal first and foremost. This group should not be about giving unsolicited advice. Advice should only be given if explicitly requested. Author and businesswoman Laila Tarraf explains, "Problem solving is the opposite of compassion. When someone

moves straight into problem solving, the other person feels judged and will not open up" (Tarraf 2021). Let people talk; often they will come to their own solutions simply as a function of feeling supported.

4. Give your group a fancy name. Because, why not? It will only add to the sense of belonging.
5. Bonus: I recommend your group comes up with a "white-flag word"—a distress signal of sorts. When trying to break free of freeze, fight, or flight, the two things we need most are social connection and movement. But when stuck in a defensive state, those are two things we absolutely cannot manage. It's beyond not feeling like it; we don't have a choice. Our biology is running the show, and being stuck perpetuates being stuck. The motivation to be active and reach out to a friend is just not available.

My Operation Springtime posse came up with a white-flag word for just those times. When someone on the team is down in the gutter and doesn't have the wherewithal to seek help, she can text the one word. It's a cry for help that doesn't require explanation or energy or clear thinking. One word. (I can't share our word; it's a secret.) You can choose any word that resonates with you and doesn't come up in regular conversation—"giraffe," for example, or "Geronimo," or "Joe Cocker" (because he sang "With a Little Help from My Friends" at Woodstock, of course).

Note: Reaching out to others to create HFFs can make us feel vulnerable. Not only because we might get turned down, but because past relationships may have left us fearful of pain or abandonment. As we practice self-regulation, healthy connections start to feel safe and supportive again. The creation of HFFs might need to be put on hold while we stabilize our nervous systems. They can be incorporated when we are ready.

Safety is a hallmark of connection. According to the Polyvagal Theory, the absence of danger is not what gives us a sense of safety; it is the presence of loving, trusting connections with others that makes us feel secure (Porges 2017, 43).

So, what happens when a relationship doesn't work? What can we do when our relationship is the source of our stress rather than a source of safety and support? Navigating disconnection is the subject of our next chapter.

CHAPTER 18

Broken Connections

We now find ourselves in a paradoxical pickle: Our species has a "biological imperative" for social connection and we humans are fabulously adept at mucking up relationships. Our connections cause disconnections. Ties to family members, work colleagues, friends, lovers, and casual acquaintances provide a collective raison d'être; however, to us as individuals, these ties can feel like aggressive games of tug-of-war.

What often fuels our mis-attunements—whether they're real or perceived—is the fear of rejection. Because we need community for survival and have an innate longing for belonging, the fear of rejection is both reasonable and powerful. In fact, our brains evolved to process social rejection and physical pain in the same cortical area (Eisenberg 2015). Disconnections can hurt in the same way a cut stings or a pulled muscle aches.

Naturally, there are times when our connections falter, and naturally those times are stressful. Stress amplifies and perpetuates the fracturing of our bonds. When we're in a fight-or-flight response, we have less patience, compassion, and empathy. Stress blurs our boundaries and makes us more critical—both of ourselves and of others. And it makes communication more challenging.

Recall from the Stress Quadrant that disconnection is a characteristic of fight-or-flight and freeze. Being stressed out makes it difficult to communicate—or even to hear each other clearly. Have you ever been arguing with someone, and you could swear they're not hearing you? It feels as if you're speaking different languages. This is a physiological phenomenon. If one or both of you are in a stress response, you cannot—biologically speaking—hear each other. Rational thinking goes out the window as well. When you're in the middle of a stress response, it's like part of your brain goes offline.

When we're unable to repair a fractured social connection, our nervous system moves into what author and clinician Deb Dana calls "patterns of protection" (Dana 2020). These are our default responses and dominant tendencies anytime we fear rejection or hurt. Strained relationships are stressful, and stress makes relationships strained—a vicious cycle, and the cause of those patterns of protection.

From the outside, these patterns look like shutting down, picking fights, appeasing someone, isolating oneself, giving someone the cold shoulder—whatever helps a person feel safe from another's potential harm. From the inside, though, these patterns feel like loneliness and pain.

Sometimes defensive armor is appropriate: If you find prejudiced words (or a piece of furniture) being hurled at you, please maintain a high-stress response until you are safe. That said, though protecting oneself is normal, defensive strategies can cripple social reconnection.

How Self-Regulation Helps Co-Regulation

We can restore damaged relationships and make peace with other people by interrupting our default patterns of protection. Repairs occur when we are regulated—when we land back in our Settled Section. In this way, settling tools can mend fences.

Brain-body mismatches occur in relationships in two counterintuitive ways: The first happens when the mind interprets "familiar" as "safe," causing us to view harmful relationships as healthy because they reflect a dynamic we recognize from childhood. The other occurs when our nervous system gets stuck in survival mode, causing us to feel unsafe even in the most secure relationships.

Thankfully, a regulated nervous system gives us insight into the true dynamics of our relationships. When we are settled, the quality of our communication improves. We can hear others better, and we can hear our own needs and wants better as well. Self-regulation—through consistent practice of settling tools—can repair the brain-body communication glitches that keep our minds in the past.

Heather's Story

My friend Heather discovered how a settled nervous system can help you determine when a relationship is no longer working. Heather had taken the

Resilience Toolkit workshop and found body-based regulation tools to be "life-changing."

Soon after completing the course, Heather met Todd. During their two-year relationship, they cooked together, attended baseball games, picnicked at the Hollywood Bowl, and traveled to Arizona and Hawaii.

In her more embodied and settled state, Heather was able to approach this relationship with greater self-awareness. She knew it wasn't a perfect match for either of them, but instead of desperately trying to force it to work by shapeshifting into someone she's not, Heather remained connected to herself. She consciously decided to take risks, staying curious and open.

When their relationship ended, Heather didn't feel the same "clawing, seething, gooey-black frantic monster" in her body that she'd felt in past breakups. Though painful, it was different. "I haven't been this clear about my needs and this able to communicate them," she noticed. "I haven't been this willing to be messy or imperfect."

Her grief over losing Todd was big, but it wasn't the crushing monster she'd experienced in the past. "I can now hold it all," Heather says. "I have a 'me' that's bigger than the pain."

Breaking Patterns of Disconnection

When I interviewed people for this book, I asked them if using calming techniques altered their interactions with others. They invariably told me stories about breaking old patterns of discord and friction in their relationships.

One of my interviewees, Denis, said he could now admit it when he inadvertently hurt someone: "I am finding apologizing a lot easier. And not apologizing with lots of explanation. Just simply apologizing and just sitting with it."

Janice described how calming with somatic tools enriched her relationships with her three siblings. It shook up their dynamics, broke old patterns, and made a world of difference in their often-intense family gatherings. "I'm able to be less reactive and less defensive," she told me. "If just one person is a little more regulated, it's better."

The Buddhist monk Thích Nhất Hạnh reminds us that calm is contagious, even under life-and-death circumstances:

> When the crowded Vietnamese refugee boats met with storms or pirates, if everyone panicked all would be lost. But if even one person on the boat remained calm and centered, it was enough. It showed the way for everyone to survive. (2023)

Racism as Disconnection

Broken connections occur not only between individuals but also between groups. Racism and other "isms" can fracture the ties within communities and between cultures. Healing and liberation from centuries-old divisions can only happen from a place of safety and regulation.

Social worker and trauma therapist Resmaa Menakem attributes racial rifts *not* to political or social issues but to visceral, body-based reactivity. As he explains in his book, *My Grandmother's Hands,* "We've tried to teach our brains to think better about race. But white-body supremacy doesn't live in our thinking brains. It lives and breathes in our bodies" (2017, 5).

Menakem points to "reflexive constrictions," which occur during racial encounters. This tightening comes from unconscious somatic sources. Because these sensations are uncomfortable, our predicting brains misinterpret them as threatening. This is the source of our continued racial strife, according to Menakem, and is, therefore, the starting point for repair:

> Most forms of dialogue, diversity training, and other cognitive interventions are going to have little effect on this reflexive fear response, because the white body has been trained to respond in this noncognitive way. (2017, 91 and 99)

Menakem shares valuable recommendations (see the Resources section) for using regulation tools to settle our bodies and minds during racially-charged encounters. We can use these on either side of an uncomfortable exchange, whether it is fraught with racism, sexism, ageism, ableism, antisemitism, homophobia, transphobia, xenophobia, or any other prejudice or fear. He emphasizes being aware of physical responses without trying to change them or run from them: "When you get the impulse to analyze or think about the discomfort, bring yourself back to the sensation of discomfort itself" (2017, 165–170). Menakem predicts that understanding and processing the "reflexive constrictions" in this way will help move the needle on collective healing.

Learning to experience discomfort without automatically assuming danger builds the capacity for reconnection and transformation. In Chapter 20, we'll walk through specific ways to signal safety to your brain and body during uncomfortable interactions.

Losing Yourself to Reach Others

In her research on connection, best-selling author Brené Brown focuses on the meaning of belonging. "True belonging," she says, "doesn't require you to change who you are; it requires you to be who you are" (Brown 2021, 158).

Indeed, we are most content in those friendships where we can be ourselves. Approaching relationships with a settled nervous system allows us to find, convey, and maintain our identity within a relationship—even for those of us (Heather and myself included) who have developed protective patterns of appeasing, fawning, or people-pleasing.

Maintaining your connection with yourself is just as important as making connections with others. But our strategies for fitting in often require us to mask—or even detach from—our authentic selves. For example, after the COVID pandemic necessitated a long pause in large social gatherings, I returned to mingling to find the social hiatus had highlighted (in bright yellow marker!) my own tendencies, making me more aware of how I interact with others.

Because I am reaching (almost out of my body) to connect with someone, I tend to lose touch with myself. My sense of what is happening in my body—my interoception—goes out the window. I disconnect from myself to connect with others.

The "out-of-body experience," if you will, would escape my attention in the moment. It would register as a lack of feeling—a mild freeze response. It wasn't until later, after leaving the party, that I became aware of the irritability I was carrying or the pain in my neck or the need to pee. I hadn't noticed any somatic cues while I was tap dancing for the other human beings. But after social events, I felt spent—exhausted, empty, and devoid of myself.

For me, the definition of "grounded" is staying in your own body *while* you are co-regulating with others. This allows for less tap dancing, more authentic connection. To counteract the disembodiment I experience at social functions, I use some of the sensory tools from Chapter 16—techniques that focus on internal sensations (interoception) and external input (exteroception) simultaneously. If I'm interacting at a gathering while seated, I keep connected with myself by feeling the chair on my thighs or the texture of my clothes on my skin. If I'm standing, I feel my feet on the ground or notice the temperature of the liquid in the glass I am holding.

I am getting better at staying in my body while socializing. I'm more aware of my feelings and thoughts. I can sense my hands and feet and a sort of mellow vibration in my body. I might notice if I am hot or cold. It's not that everything feels good. It just feels. My interoceptive faculties are operational—all systems go.

Human connections are difficult. However, through regulation, we improve our communication with others and develop clarity about the integrity of our relationships. We sense our own body and stay connected to our authentic selves. We "infect" others who are stressed and disconnected, guiding them to calmer waters. Most importantly, we distinguish uncomfortable feelings from danger signals, mending racial conflict and building connections that are more empathetic, authentic, and compassionate—the way human connections were designed to be.

Unavoidable Connections

One type of relationship—that of parent and child—seems particularly challenging, especially rewarding, and certainly deserving of a more in-depth look, which is why parenting is the topic of our next chapter.

CHAPTER 19

Parenting

Volcanos are geological escape hatches through which pressure is released from a rupture at Mother Earth's core. When activated, they can result in huge consequences for those in their path.

For a while, volcanos of all kinds were a big part of my friend Arrowyn Ambrose's life. Her daughter, who goes by Pony, developed a fascination with Pompeii, the ancient Italian city preserved under volcanic ash. Arrowyn, a fellow Resilience Toolkit facilitator, spent much of her time watching Pompeii documentaries with Pony and having discussions with her about volcanos.

Pony was a notoriously picky eater, and one day she refused to eat the black beans Arrowyn had so lovingly soaked overnight and cooked in the morning. Mommy lost it! She screamed and slammed a door (or two). "There's nothing like parenting to blow your top!" she told me. And she's right.

Let's face it, parenting is stressful. It's a game of uncertainty and ambiguity (there's that loathsome word again). My controlling nature was outmatched when I became a mother. So I read all the books—*Happiest Baby on the Block, What to Expect the First Year, Breastfeed Your Way to an Ivy League Kid* (okay, that one's a joke)—and tried all the techniques, hoping to win "Mother of the Year." Eventually, though, I threw away all my how-to-parent books. They were making me more rigid, throwing me into perpetual mommy anxiety, and interfering with my intuitive ability to bond with my bundle of joy.

Newborn to Eight Years Old

Co-regulation is particularly important between parents and children. This symbiotic relationship will ebb and flow as the pair moves in and out of connection with each other. But before the age of nine, children's nervous systems emulate those of the adults in their lives. In the early stages of development, children usually cannot be more regulated than their primary caretaker. Think about it: Have you ever seen a young child remain calm and relaxed when the adult they rely on is in a state of frantic distress? An anxious parent will generally result in an anxious or frozen child. Children mirror their caregiver's state of regulation. A baby's best lullaby is the lull of an adult's settled nervous system.

Slumber is often a big topic for new parents and a source of much stress and vexation. Joanna Clark, owner of Blissful Baby Sleep Coaching (see the Resources section), helps families with children between six months and six years of age catch more Zs at nighttime and naptime. Using the Gentle Sleep Coaching™ method created by family therapist Kim West, Joanna has worked with thousands of struggling households. "The families that come to me, come to me in crisis where their child is not sleeping," Joanna tells me. "Bedtime is typically a nightmare. The child wakes up multiple times a night, does not take naps, and the entire family system is disrupted."

Joanna's approach is an alternative to "cry-it-out" methods and focuses instead on the parent-child bond. As I talk with her, it's clear how much empathy and compassion she has for her clients. She herself grappled with sleep deprivation while her children were young, and she understands what it can do to someone's mental and physical wellbeing. She paints a vivid description of what families seeking her services are going through:

> Frustrated [and] overwhelmed, they're arguing about what to do about the sleep situation. One parent is typically taking the burden of the nighttime caregiving, which builds resentment inside the marriage. There's a lot of helplessness and hopelessness around how to solve it. The mom is filled with guilt, which is usually accompanied with shame. She often feels like a "bad mom" because she can't figure out how to help her child sleep well. And so, the mom will martyr herself by doing more and more and more and more—more rocking, more bouncing, more nursing, more co-sleeping, more attending in the middle of the night. And so, what happens to the mom is that she becomes extremely hypervigilant, overwhelmed, and sleep-deprived.

I asked Joanna how this affects a parent's ability to soothe a child. She tells me that I have hit on her main area of focus. Having a regulated parent means the "bedtime routine is a calm and, key word here," she pauses for effect, "'emotionally connected' time."

"Emotionally connected" can't happen if you are in a state of stress. Of course, being stressed-out is inevitable in parenting. But becoming grounded would have made my early parenting more gratifying for me *and* my son. It would have fortified my endurance of endless diaper changes, countless worries, and sleepless nights. Perhaps it would have lightened the inevitable self-doubt about my mothering qualifications. Many of my colleagues who learned self-regulation tools *after* raising their children have echoed the same sentiment. Their parenting cup was often too empty to enjoy the baby phase, and self-regulating tools would have been helpful in refilling their reservoirs.

Please note: Just because I'm saying children under the age of nine are most influenced by the nervous-system states of their caretakers, does not mean I am placing blame on parents. The inherent protection mechanisms of guardianship (not to mention an increasingly antagonistic world) trigger our high-alert survival system. The more we try to be perfect parents (there's no such thing, by the way), the more our fight-or-flight systems get activated.

So there's no blame. Being stressed as a parent is natural and common. The idea is to seek moments of regulation, creating an affirming child-parent relationship for all involved.

Rupture and Repair

Arrowyn was fortunate. When Pony refused to eat her yummy beans and rice, Arrowyn had body-based tools at her disposal. She knew she needed to address her knee-jerk reaction—the yelling and the dramatic door-slamming. This common parent-child dance is often called "rupture and repair." Arrowyn recalls, "I realized that I had to repair, but as a parent, I can't repair from that state. Trying to repair when you're still agitated, that's really hard."

She extracted herself from the room and used a self-regulation tool to settle her nervous system before returning, apologizing, and mending the ruptured connection. "I realized how much more capacity I have to be curious and not take things personally when I'm more settled and aware of my state," she says.

Later that day, Pony presented her mom with a crayon drawing of an erupting volcano. In big, bold letters across the top, the title read: "The Eruption of Mommycano!"

Making Matters Worse

When children have medical issues, a parent's regulation becomes even more hard-won. A child's behavior, tantrums, or anxiety might have a genetic or physiological explanation that has nothing to do with a parent's nervous-system state. A preterm baby, for example, does not have a fully developed calming nervous system, as this occurs in the last trimester of gestation. Stephen Porges explains how this can affect both child and parent:

> A preterm infant's depressed social engagement system will have a negative impact on caregivers, who are anticipating reciprocal cues of social connection via facial expressivity and prosodic vocalizations. The result may be a parent who feels they love their child, but their child does not love them. (2021, 4)

Thankfully, we can still benefit from teaching our parenting brains to feel safer and, therefore, more settled. A parent's ability to temper their own temper during their child's outburst often dictates whether the child's discomfort will escalate or subside.

Monica's Story

Monica's son, Evan, was three years old when his struggles first appeared. As she describes it:

> He used to get extraordinarily dysregulated, just total overwhelm of big physical feelings, big emotions, and he would stop making eye contact. He would flail around. He sometimes would start throwing things, and he would stop using words. He would just start yelling.

At first Monica resorted to parenting methods she learned from her own mother and father:

> If I had big emotions, they would just yell at me. Tell me to go to my room, just shut it down. And that didn't teach me anything about how

> to process what I was going through, how to soothe myself in a healthy way.

By the time Evan was five, Monica found a different approach. She began using body-based calming tools to help herself and him, and she immediately saw a change. "He still gets dysregulated, but it doesn't escalate as much, and I have tools to settle myself and then to settle him," she says.

"Looking back, I was in a chronic state of anxiety," she recalls, "and not able to ground myself—not able to calm myself."

Monica used tools like the ones in this book to self-regulate, but when I asked her about helping Evan regulate, she said, "I love to sing, and so, if my son's calm enough, I'll try to sing. But then if he's really heightened, rocking and humming... are very grounding." This is a process known as "vagal toning."

Vagal Toning

Vagal tone is the term used to describe the overall function and health of your vagus nerve (the tenth cranial nerve). Higher vagal tone indicates your calming nervous system is in good working order—that it's interacting properly with your heart, immune system, digestive system, and other areas of the body. Lower vagal tone is associated with health risks, increased sensitivity to stress, and poor recovery from stress.

Vagal tone can be measured indirectly via heart rate variability (HRV). As you may recall from Chapter 15, HRV measures the variations in length of time between heartbeats. *Higher HRV means higher vagal tone*. It is an indication of a healthy balance between the Stillness System and the Movement System.

Tracking HRV has become easier with the invention of wearable technology which can monitor heart rate. An Oura ring, disguised as a piece of jewelry, tracks my HRV while I sleep. There's no standard or optimal HRV to target. You can't compare your own HRV with someone else's—even of your same age and gender. Instead, you'll want to find your own personal baseline and see what external factors (sleep, food, stress, noise, relaxation, etc.) affect its upward or downward trajectory.

One way to improve your vagal tone and increase your HRV is to stimulate the vagus nerve via humming, singing, or gargling. These activities have two stress-reducing mechanisms at play: They slow our breathing, extending the exhalation (which we discussed in Chapter 12), and they produce vibrations in our face and vocal cords. Remember the quartet of nerves from Chapter 2? Singing, humming, and gargling stimulating those vagal-connected cranial nerve—like playing soothing music on the strings of our vagal violin.

Anything generating vibration in the face (like singing or humming) can activate the vagus nerve and help reduce stress. One study found decreased stress markers and increased feelings of joy and elation after six months of singing lessons. The test subjects also showed an uptick in oxytocin, a feel-good hormone related to social connection and bonding (Grape et al. 2002). A humming technique in yoga called Bhramari Pranayama or "bee-breath," also reduces stress by increasing HRV through vibration (Ghati et al. 2021).

Children naturally sing and hum when they're happy. By following her motherly instincts to sing and hum with Evan, Monica sent safety signals to both their nervous systems. Plus, improvements in a parent's vagal tone may also have beneficial effects on their child's emotional development (Perlman, Camras, and Pelphrey 2008). By choosing activities her son could participate in, Monica extended him a co-regulation olive branch of connection, calm, and emotional wellbeing.

Seeking Help Requires a Settled Nervous System

As Monica prepared to send her son off to kindergarten, she discovered that advocating for Evan could also be anxiety-provoking. She needed to research special-education accommodations and occupational therapy, decide which school would be a good fit, and consider whether insurance would cover costs.

"It's such a nightmare to sift through all that stuff," Monica shares. "I found a lot of moments of that process to trigger my anxiety more. You know, getting the help you need to get out of anxiety can be anxiety-inducing."

Learning how to self-regulate improves a parent's ability to seek assistance and advocate for their child's needs. When we're exasperated, the way forward is unclear—but settling our nervous system enhances our ability to clearly see the right path.

How to Bee-Breathe:

- Sitting comfortably, place your thumbs in your ears and your fingers over your closed eyes. Alternatively, your hands can rest in your lap.
- Keeping your mouth closed, inhale through your nose.
- As you exhale through your nose, make a humming sound in the back of your throat. Exhale for as long as possible without straining.
- Repeat as many times as you like, usually three to ten times.

Nine and Up

As children outgrow their princess dresses and toy trains (as they do), they develop more independence, not only in their activities but also in their nervous systems.

Around the time a child is blowing out nine candles on their birthday cake, their brain's frontal lobes are becoming more fully developed. This allows for better self-monitoring and enhanced personality development. During this phase of maturation, children begin to separate their identities from those of their caregivers. They start to distinguish their own state of relaxation or stress from the states of those around them. They find their autonomous place on the Stress Quadrant.

A More Settled Symbiosis

Parenting is hard. Like Arrowyn and many others, I *still* turn into a "mommycano" sometimes. But I have learned to relax into parenthood a little more. Improved somatic awareness has helped me approach all of my partnerships from a more settled place. In the next chapter, I share some of my favorite ways to support and sustain relationships—whether they are with family members, friends, lovers, or others.

CHAPTER 20

Improving Relationships

Whenever I get upset about something a loved one has done, I play a little game called "Barometer or Brat."

I used to believe my teenage son's procrastination automatically set me off. One day he came to me for last-minute help putting together a costume for a school performance. And I do mean last minute. He had ignored the responsibility until the night before the show. I blew up! Full-on mommycano moment. (Thank you, dear Pony from the last chapter, for such an apropos term.)

But here's the interesting thing: He had done something similar two weeks prior, and I'd reacted in a completely different way. I'd been standing in the same place in the den, similarly engrossed in something, yet I'd only smiled at his tendency to procrastinate and drove him to the store for the needed supplies.

Whether his behavior was irresponsible is beside the point (we can tackle the subject of teens with attention-deficit disorder in a different book). The point is, I had two markedly different reactions to almost identical situations. The deciding factor? *My* place on the Stress Quadrant when he asked me for help. He wasn't necessarily being a "brat." He wasn't provoking my hidden "bad" side. His behavior was acting as a barometer for the state of my nervous system. The storm was already brewing; my son didn't create the weather.

When I am in a fight-or-flight state (jazz hands!), my family gets the reactive, quick-to-anger mom. When I have more freeze energy, they get the disengaged, spaced-out mom. It doesn't matter what *they* do; my arousal state dictates my reaction. Generally, my response is not an indicator of their disrespect, rudeness, or fill-in-the blank; it is an indicator that I'm stressed—that my nervous system is anticipating a threat behind every door, and someone just happened to open one. It means I haven't been consistent with my self-regulation tools (such as those shared in Chapters 12 to 16).

We tend to blow up at the people closest to us—not just our children, but our parents and partners as well. Around them, we feel safe enough to show our "true selves." Although, really what we are showing is not our authenticity but our current stress level. When a loved one gets a big rise out of us, it might be more about where we are parked on the Stress Quadrant than about their behavior. So, if a situation riles you up, playing "Barometer or Brat" can determine if you need to settle your nervous system.

How to Play:

1. Excuse yourself from the interaction so you can be alone.

2. Check in with yourself. Where are you currently on the Stress Quadrant? More importantly, where were you on the Quadrant before the incident? In place of the Stress Quadrant, you can give your stress level a number on a scale of one to ten.
3. If appropriate, try a quick settling tool (see the final chapter).
4. Once you have noted a little settling within your system, consider the following questions: Do you still feel as offended, irritated, or enraged? When you think about the other person's actions, words, or point of view, do you now have more understanding or less?

Abusive Relationships

There are exceptions to what I am talking about—times when getting angry and upset is more appropriate than staying calm and cool. People can do abhorrent things, warranting a stress response. If someone is being mentally or physically abused, for example, calming down would not help them. Remember, the golden rule of self-regulation is to only use a settling tool when it is safe to do so. In a potentially dangerous situation, stress responses are a reasonable reflex.

Sometimes, however, we don't realize we are in a dangerous situation. If we're being mistreated, manipulated, or isolated from our family and friends (as is common in abusive relationships), the loud feelings of alarm in our bodies can be overwhelming. We may have no choice but to shut down and dissociate. Because our bodies hold our truths, this turning off of the body's messages means we no longer "hear" our truth. After all, it is our bodies' stress responses that tell us when our boundaries have been crossed.

If our bodies are no longer part of the dialogue, we get the "truth" from outside ourselves. Other people's beliefs and judgments are all we have to go on—and it's usually the abuser's hurtful, self-serving words we internalize: "You are a terrible person. This is your fault. You deserve this. You can't live without me."

In abusive relationships, disembodiment may be necessary to stay safe. Unfortunately, this creates a chasm in which we accept poisonous words as fact. When the body's truth compass is frozen, it becomes inoperable—unable to lead us away from perpetrators. Returning to our bodies during safe moments (however brief) can help recalibrate our truth compass and propel us from freeze to flight.

If you are being mentally or physically abused, you can contact One Love Foundation for help. Their information is listed in the Resources section.

Difficult Relationships

Even in strained relationships that are not abusive, we may still shut off from the truth manifesting in our bodies. In *Untamed*, author Glennon Doyle writes about the moment she finally accepted the truth her mind had refused to believe—that it was time to leave her husband. Specifically, she says, "I started paying close attention to patterns in my body, because my body often clarifies for me what my mind is too convoluted and hopeful to accept" (2020, 262).

Many women have been taught to suppress their emotions to keep everyone around them happy—harmony in the household takes precedence over harmony within themselves. Thankfully, this is beginning to change, however slowly.

To survive in her marriage, my friend Nancy closed herself off from her body (and her truth) for many years. In her attempt to find herself again, she sought the help of a psychologist. Nancy recounted to me the story of her second visit to this new therapist, who started the session by asking her, "How are you feeling today?"

The question stunned Nancy. Having routinely disregarded her own physical and emotional state, Nancy had no idea how to answer. "I don't know," was all she could muster.

"Well, I mean, tell me a feeling you're having," the therapist persisted.

Nancy continued the story:

> I was like, "I can't." And she got out this kindergarten thing. It said "happy," "sad," "mad." And she said, "Could you pick a word from this list?" And I was like, "Nope." She said, "Do you think maybe 'sad'?"

That day in therapy, Nancy cried—for the first time in twelve years.

She can now look back at her marriage:

> When I asked about certain things in my relationship, I was steered off course so that I didn't

> find out the truth. So, I was suppressing those feelings. I didn't cry. I didn't cry. I didn't cry. I didn't cry. I lost my way. I felt what was my children's heartbreak, felt my husband's stress, felt my parents' stress, but I didn't make time for mine. Mainly because when I tried to, I was told, "You're better than that. You're bigger than that. You're stronger than that."

Talk therapy helped Nancy. But it was when she reconnected with her body and rekindled trust in her soul speak (its murmurs and its screams) that her healing journey really took off.

Stress Language Fluency

In his book, *The Five Love Languages*, Dr. Gary Chapman organizes the universal ways of communicating love into five categories: words of affirmation, quality time, receiving gifts, acts of service, and physical touch. He found we each have one or two ways we prefer receiving expressions of love. By learning and speaking each other's favored love languages, partners can fill their "love tanks" and maintain uplifting relationships (Chapman 2015).

I found the concept of love languages to be really helpful in my marriage. Perhaps just as enlightening was learning to use my two primary love languages (quality time and physical touch, in case you're curious) to communicate self-love. Quality alone time speaks volumes to my soul. And physical touch through massage, hot baths, and (my new favorite morning routine) dry brushing can also help me show love towards myself.

In our relationships "stress languages" may be just as eye-opening as "love languages." I created stress languages as a way of exploring our partner's (as well as our own) default tendencies—those patterns of protection we talked about in Chapter 18. Becoming aware of your partner's go-to stress response (i.e., where they tend to spend time on the Stress Quadrant) can bring empathy, respect, and deeper connection. Using labels is generally not my favorite thing to do, but these labels create a shared language for comforting—not fixing or judging—one another. Stress languages build understanding and acceptance and help us recognize when our loved ones need extra support.

Most people have more than one stress language. They toggle between them, often within the same day—or even the same minute. Occasionally, two of the stress languages may blend into one. A person might even speak one stress language among siblings and a different one with intimate partners. Our five stress languages can be personified as follows.

1. The Fixer: A doer who goes into immediate action. Whether in the mode of "tend-or-befriend" or "fight-or-flight," the Fixer has difficulty slowing down—even when it's time to sleep.

2. The Numb-er: A user of distractions like drugs, alcohol, sex, TV, gaming, compulsive exercising—even long hours at the office can be a form of numbing. Workaholism is a common Numb-er strategy.

3. The Exploder: A catastrophizer who sees everything as a crisis, reacts with rage or paranoia, searches for someone to blame, or has a strong urge to escape from stressful environments.

4. The Imploder: An internalizer who responds with paralysis, helplessness, depression, or self-blame. The Imploder may be unable to make eye contact or express emotions and may feel no choice but to cope by ignoring or "ghosting" people. The Imploder may also dissociate from their own feelings and body sensations.

5. The Denier: A wearer of many hats. The Denier can look like an extreme blind-to-reality optimist, a stoic shunning all emotion, or a fountain of toxic positivity. The Denier may bottle up all their feelings until forcing themselves into Exploder or Imploder territory.

Understanding Each Other's Stress Languages

My husband is an Imploder and a Numb-er. I used to get upset when he'd put up what felt like a wall between us. I would try to knock it down by nagging him about the wall (insert face-palm emoji here!). Now that I have names for his stress languages, I have a bird's-eye view of what is happening: An Imploder wall or some Numb-er overworking signals me to give him extra love, support, and space.

Vanessa, a mom familiar with the Stress Quadrant, taught the concept to her eleven-year-old daughter, Silvia. Speaking to me from her home in Amsterdam, Vanessa explains how understanding each other's stress languages has improved their mother-daughter relationship:

> I tend to go into dissociation, and she tends to go more into fight-or-flight. So, we can see that now. Nobody's doing anything wrong; we just have different stress responses. So, we can have a conversation. I think even just realizing what's happening, and being able to name it, and then developing a shared language around it is helpful.

Just acknowledging one another's stress languages goes a long way toward breaking patterns of protection and generating mutual respect and support.

Understanding Your Own Stress Language

I am a Fixer. Knowing this about myself provides a form of self-care and an opportunity for growth. Out of nowhere, I will obsess over other people's "problems" and try to fix what doesn't need fixing or what isn't mine to fix—my husband's health, my son's grades, my colleague's financial woes, my friend's love life. I have gotten better at recognizing and controlling this coping strategy. It serves me in times of real turbulence, but when my stress is chronic, and my nervous system is stuck in hyperdrive, it just creates more trouble for myself and those around me.

Tools to Reconnect and Repair

Before looking at specific tools for relationship strife, first things first: Are you in danger? If so, please do not try to settle your nervous system. If you are not safe, a heightened stress response is appropriate and helpful. But if you are safe, and you just need ways to improve your communication and connections with others, read on....

Preparing for a Difficult Encounter

If you're *in the middle* of a difficult interaction, you can step away and try any of the settling tools you've already learned. Excusing yourself to the restroom is one way to do so. You can also use the tools ahead of time to prepare yourself for a challenging situation or conversation. Settling in advance can help your body understand the difference between being uncomfortable and being in danger. Plus, pre-settling will also naturally help you hear and communicate better, which can improve the outcomes of difficult encounters.

Settling During a Difficult Encounter

The key to finding common ground when you're in an argument is to feel safe *during* the interaction. Giving your body specific safety signals helps you manage the discomfort of disconnection without generating counterproductive responses.

1. Slow Down: Slowness signals safety. Slowing down—both your movements and your breathing—indicates to your nervous system that you're not in harm's way. I don't mean so slow that you cartoonishly reenact a slow-motion video (although that might lighten up an otherwise tense

exchange!). Think of this as a *subtle* reduction in the speed of your movements.

2. Expand Your Vision: The panoramic vision exercise from Chapter 16 (also found in the concluding chapter) is perfect to use here. When we're in the middle of a fight, our visual field usually narrows. Changing from hyper-focused tunnel vision to a diffused, expansive view disrupts that pattern. Opening up your focus to include your peripheral vision communicates safety to your system.
3. Mirror Breath: Try to match the other person's breathing rhythm—practicing conscious "entrainment." If their breathing pace is fast and erratic, mirror it for a moment. Then slow down your breathing and see if they follow suit.
4. Lower Your Pitch: When you are stressed, your voice becomes higher, due to increased contraction in the throat muscles (Kozlowska et al. 2015). Purposely lowering the pitch of your voice can signal safety to the brain, decreasing the defensive responses that prevent reconnection.

The Final Say

Relationships are hard. They require a settled nervous system. Part of my evolution into non-reactive mom/wife/friend/daughter/sister came from using settling tools. Another part came from adjusting my relationship to time. Rushing is stressing (at least to my nervous system). Time to hurry over to the next chapter to learn the art of rushing.

Step Eight:

Befriend Uncomfortable

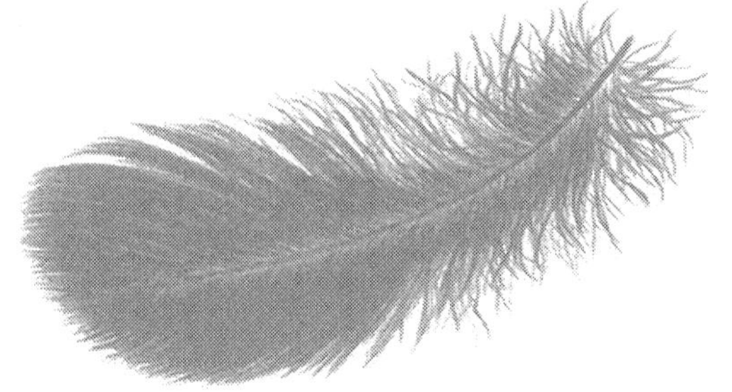

CHAPTER 21

The Art of Rushing

Urgency is in our DNA.

The pace of our lives can be dizzying. It's a testament to human passion—this fervor for maximizing experiences and outmaneuvering limitations. But when we are moving at blurring speeds, our body-minds can't always tell if we are embracing the delight of life or running from a lion.

Here's an illustration from my own experience:

I was excited to be heading out of town for a special celebration, a long weekend with some old friends at a spectacular Airbnb. My husband and I were packed and ready to hit the road, but we first needed to stock up on supplies and appetizers (I make a killer charcuterie plate!). I was eager to get to our desert retreat (complete with stunning views from the hot tub), but because I was rushing around the grocery store, my mind erroneously thought I was stressed out. I didn't realize it at the time, but I had contracted a bad case of faulty neuroception. Even though I was safe, my predicting brain misinterpreted the signals from my rushing body as signs of danger. By the time my husband and I were driving down I-10 towards Joshua Tree, my shoulders were achy, my heart was racing, and my mood had soured.

The Way Home

Hurrying has always confused my nervous system. Becoming a parent only intensified this—particularly when I was wearing my mommy-chauffeur hat. Throughout my son's childhood, I drove him to countless birthday parties, martial arts classes, tennis lessons, soccer practices, baseball games, theater productions, and so on. It didn't matter what the class or event was; what mattered was the direction—whether we were driving to it or coming home from it. On our way to the activity, the atmosphere would be tense. We rode in stiff silence or argued about undone homework and neglected chores. The drive home would be distinctly different. The atmosphere was lighter, our connection healthier. We would joke and laugh and talk about friends and experiences. The way home was always better. It took me years just to notice this pattern—and even longer to figure out why it was happening.

On the way home we weren't in a rush.

Our relationship with time depends on where we are on the Stress Quadrant. Being stuck in the upper areas of the Movement System (i.e., jazz hands!) speeds up our sense of time. An emergency or deadline can shrink hours into minutes and minutes into seconds so we are in a perpetual rush. If you are a parent, you may have noticed when you're trying to leave the house, you will—invariably, inevitably, and despite all your best intentions—be running late. I didn't have any external factors for being stressed out as I chauffeured Aidan around town, but we were certainly running late. And that, my dear friends, was enough to confuse my brain into thinking I was in fight-or-flight. My nervous system state, an overreaction to the spike in adrenaline as we hurried out the door, affected my connection with my son during those precious days of his childhood.

I am eternally grateful I learned about body-based tools while Aidan was still in middle school. Through the lens of the Polyvagal Theory, I was able to notice my over-response to rushing. I could examine the way it hampered my ability to relish life and how it negatively affected my co-regulation with my child. I was able to correct the mismatch between my brain and body and find my way home, so to speak.

Go Slow, Slowly

Even when we are trying to slow down, our bodies may continue telling us that we are rushed. Somatic habits can overpower mental determination—especially if our efforts are abrupt and haphazard.

Author and *Hurry Slowly* podcast host Jocelyn K. Glei once worked at an exciting start-up. She loved her job. In fact, she loved it too much, as she describes in her article, "Confessions of a Burnt Out Over-Achiever." She writes, "I had produced a shit-ton of incredible things, but I was a burnt out husk of a person."

Glei realized she was no longer maintaining friendships, exercising, or eating right. She had stopped doing anything besides work. As she puts it, "I wasn't listless or unproductive or disengaged from my work. The problem was: *All I was engaged with was my work.* And that was causing me to work in a way that was utterly unsustainable" (Glei 2022).

She decided to slow down. However, despite her efforts, Glei noticed her body was having trouble catching on to the new program:

> For six months after I slowed down, I woke up with a strange buzzing sensation, my body thrumming with energy. Stuck in a rhythm after years of overwork, my body was continuing to release the excess amount of adrenaline that I had previously needed to get through the day. (Glei 2022)

This is what I would call "delayed neuroception." Her body needed time—and help—adjusting to the change.

Determined to match her somatic sensations to her new cognitive slowdown, Glei enlisted the help of both mind-focused and body-focused professionals. She reached out to a psychotherapist, physical therapist (yes!), acupuncturist, life coach, personal trainer, Reiki practitioner, even a shaman. Glei created a consortium of support to correct the mismatch between her desire to reclaim her life and her body's reluctance to relinquish the adrenaline dependence. This deceleration team helped guide her through the process, which can otherwise be bumpy and confusing.

Happy in Haste

A state of slow calm doesn't always feel good (recall the Stillness Seesaw). We can become at home with the hurry and that familiar frantic feeling. It can be difficult to trust the softening—to know you can come to a rest and still be okay. For me, stillness can be a reminder of the paralysis I experienced when going through depression in my early twenties. I need to go slow when I slow down. This helps decouple the calmer pace from a frozen inability to function. Baby steps. Titration is key.

We live in a caffeinated society that confuses slowing down with laziness. Our culture teaches us to be wary of a relaxed pace and to feel more important, worthy, and protected when we are rushing around being busy. *Do Nothing* author Celeste Headlee explains:

> We have been deluded by the forces of economics and religion to believe that the purpose of life is hard work. So, every time we feel empty, dissatisfied or unfulfilled, we work harder and put in more hours. (2020, xiv)

Our culture has a history of condemning the necessary reprieves of rest and recovery. In a 2022 op-ed piece for the *New York Times*, Rabbi Elliot Kukla looks at the historical roots of our concept of laziness:

> Shunning laziness is integral to the American dream. The Puritans who colonized New

> England believed that laziness led to damnation. They used this theology to justify their enslavement of Black people, whose souls they claimed to have "saved" by turning them into productive laborers.

Our fear of sloth—one of the seven deadly sins—has turned us into a clan of over-doers. Our busyness has become a source of false value and artificial salvation.

Fast and Furious

My elderly neighbor Pearl understands the truth about rushing. She senses its blunt, staccato nature. She and I often encounter each other during my daily dog walks. Halo, our yellow lab, is now fourteen years old and slower than Pearl. "I could walk *that* dog," she tells me.

Pearl walks this same street every day. "How often do you walk up and down?" I asked her recently.

"Ten times in the morning and ten times after dinner," she replied. Pearl doesn't like to veer off onto adjoining streets. Her street has a high wall along the sidewalk where she can sit whenever she feels the need. She had a knee replacement several years ago, and she's in her nineties.

Over her usual all-white outfit, Pearl wore a cardigan decorated with the colorfully embroidered names and cartoon faces of her five grandchildren. It was Monday, and she grimaced at the cars zooming past us. "They are much nicer on weekends," she said, reaching down to pet my dog.

"Do they wave to you on weekends?" I asked, assuming such a stable fixture of this small town might elicit greetings from strangers and acquaintances alike.

"No," she said quickly. "They just drive slower."

When we are rushed, we are stressed. Our patience is on pause. Empathy diminishes, and irritability takes over. This is why Pearl can tell, just by the number on your speedometer, whether you are feeling cordial or callous.

Halo agrees with Pearl on this. On the days when I am relaxed, her snail's pace is cute and I relish our slow walks together. On the days when I am rushed, however, her long sniffing rituals exasperate me and she gets tugged along by her leash as I try to pick up the pace.

Settling Is Slowing

Deceleration can be a shaky endeavor. When you have been moving at top speed, slamming on the brakes isn't as effective as pumping them intermittently to gradually slow down. It's not easy, which is why airplane passengers often applaud when the pilot executes a smooth, non-jerky landing. To slow down evenly, of course, you need to settle your nervous system. For Glei, the therapy team she amassed functioned as a gentle, incremental braking system, which helped provide her with a smoother landing. Perhaps this is the most effective way to manage in a world that encourages rushing.

You may feel resistant to this idea of slowing down. We often tell ourselves things like, "When I have more money, then I will rest." Usually, though, the more money we have, the *less* free time we get: "Over the past twenty or thirty years, the people who used to work all the time (the lower earners) are now the ones with more time to spare, while upper income brackets are overscheduled" (Headlee 2020, 48).

So, our scramble persists, and our obsession with the distant horizon—that urgent need to get to the next level in life—only perpetuates that scramble. In *Four Thousand Weeks: Time Management for Mortals*, Oliver Burkeman counsels:

> In a world geared for hurry, the capacity to resist the urge to hurry—to allow things to take the time they take—is a way to gain purchase on the world, to do the work that counts, and to derive satisfaction from the doing itself, instead of deferring all your fulfillment to the future. (2021, 174)

Rushing ourselves (and our kids) in an effort to create a more perfect future is a stress response born out of uncertainty about tomorrow. When we allow ourselves to settle and regulate, we let go of the need to bullishly charge through life. We give ourselves relief from the incessant pressure to fill even our leisure time with self-improvement projects. Settling diverts our focus away from the future and returns us to the present moment. There is nothing to rush towards. We are already there.

Rushing Reset

The following technique helps me recalibrate my nervous system. I use it when I need to tell my mind that, despite an uptick in adrenaline, I'm safe (just running late). I also use it when I need help feeling secure while slowing down. I call this exercise "alternating squeezes."

You can use any of the tools in Part 2 to help you reset during times of haste; however, this tool feels particularly apropos. It takes less than thirty seconds (so you won't be *more delayed* to that meeting or Elmo birthday party), and it can be done before walking out the door or before starting up the car. It's also great during the holidays or when a work deadline is stressing you out. Or you can use it to get your body to relax at the start of a vacation.

Alternating Squeezes

- You can be sitting or standing for this exercise.
- Start by using your right hand to gently squeeze your left arm just below the shoulder. Hold this squeeze for a couple of seconds. Don't forget to keep breathing
- Move your right hand down a couple of inches so that it's just above your left elbow and squeeze again. Hold that squeeze for a second or two.
- Move it down again to just above the wrist (you can bend your elbow if you wish). Squeeze and hold, being sure not to hold your breath.
- Repeat the entire sequence on the opposite side, with your left hand squeezing your right arm:

- Just below the shoulder, squeeze and hold.
  Just above the elbow, squeeze and hold.
  Just above the wrist, squeeze and hold.

Note: The areas on the arm where I have guided you to squeeze are not set in stone. You can choose to squeeze anywhere along your arm that feels right for you. However, crossing the midline of the body (hand across to opposite arm) is important as it helps with the calming effect.

You can do this same technique using your legs. While sitting, bring your right hand to your left upper thigh. Squeeze and hold for a couple of seconds. Repeat this squeeze-and-hold process at the middle of your thigh and again just above your knee. Then repeat the sequence using your left hand on your right leg.

Driven to Rush

Goals and aspirations fuel much of our hustle. No matter which ladder you are climbing, you're most likely trying to scurry to the top as expeditiously as possible. Slowing down or stopping to take in the view isn't generally part of the goal process.

Striving may be part of human nature, but it is also stressful. So how do we reconcile our need to slow down with our passionate drive to push ourselves into the uncomfortable? That is the topic of our next two chapters.

CHAPTER 22

Pushing into Uncomfortable

Writing a book about stress is stressful. Ironic, I know!

When I settled on writing *Settled* (sorry—couldn't help myself), I knew it would be a push into some uncomfortable feelings and body sensations. I wondered if I could stay grounded through the grind. Could I embrace striving without stressing? These are usually linked for me. What if the book is an utter failure? What if only my mother reads it? (Love you, Mom!)

Over the past ten years, I allowed stress sensitivity to keep me from thriving, and I knew I needed to change that. I had something to say, and I had to get uncomfortable in order to say it. I needed to embrace the vulnerability of calling myself an author. So I signed up for a writing course, during which... you publish a book.

As you may recall, acute stress increases your motivation and focus. So, when you tackle a big goal—such as writing a book—you start out with a whole lot of drive, excitement, and persistence. But as the journey drags on (and on), and life's other stressors come into play, your stress goes from acute to chronic. Setting out toward an ambitious goal means setting out a welcome mat for uncomfortableness. It involves giving yourself a deliberate push out of your comfort zone. If that uncomfortableness becomes chronic, it opens a floodgate of stress responses that can shut down your aspirations.

Holy Frit

Tim Carey's big goal was huge—an art project nearly the size of a basketball court. An artistic director for a stained-glass company, Carey won a commission to produce the largest stained-glass window in the world: a whopping 3,400 square-foot biblical tableau for a Methodist Church in Leawood, Kansas.

The design Carey pitched to the church involved a glasswork method he didn't even know how to use yet. And he and his crew faced a tight deadline if they were to complete the project without financial penalties.

Filmmaker Justin Monroe, Carey's next-door neighbor, captured the monumental undertaking in his documentary *Holy Frit.* "Frit" refers to the fusible ground glass Carey would need to learn to use before he could execute his winning design. Instead of just the separated colors of traditional stained glass, his "Resurrection Window" would have to rely on layers of textured color to achieve its intricate effects.

Enter Narcissus Quagliata, a virtuoso in the world of glass art. Quagliata joined forces with Carey to teach him his fusion technique, and their team managed to complete the church's "Resurrection Window" in time for Easter Sunday of 2017. However, as Monroe's film depicts, Carey's magnificent goal took a significant toll. His nutrition suffered. He stopped exercising. He lost sleep. And when he did sleep, he would break out into a cold sweat. The film shows tension and friction developing between Carey and his co-workers. As his boss said to the camera, "Tim's a mess" (Monroe 2021, 42:49).

How Goals Create Stress Responses

Reaching for goals complicates life. You invite problems in, and other activities—including activities that relieve stress—take a backseat. For Tim Carey, that meant putting everything on hold to finish the biggest project of his life. Well, almost everything. But we'll get to that in the next chapter.

Goals are mostly about pushing. And when your nervous system senses pushing, it pushes back. It doesn't care if the change is good or bad. Change involves the unfamiliar, and the nervous system interprets that as a threat—even if you're moving towards a more fulfilling, pleasant, or peaceful life. Disrupting the status quo throws you into survival mode. As a safety measure, your mind gets stuck in patterns designed to minimize growth: You procrastinate, tell yourself you're not ready, and wait endlessly for the "perfect" time to start. Self-sabotage is a stress response. It is trying to protect you.

The Satisfaction Mirage

In Western medicine, we evaluate a patient's cardiovascular system using a "stress test." This procedure is commonly administered by having the patient walk or run on a treadmill. In this case, the treadmill is the stressor.

Most of our everyday-life stressors come from a treadmill of sorts: the constant running towards future success in an endless pursuit of accolades, wealth, and prestige.

Our human biology perpetuates this hedonic treadmill through the neurotransmitter dopamine. Since we mistakenly associate it with pleasure, dopamine is referred to as the "feel-good hormone." However, in their book, *The Molecule of More*, Daniel Z. Lieberman and Michael E. Long offer an important clarification: Dopamine is about desire. The brain starts releasing dopamine when an enticing possibility dangles in front of us like a carrot. It keeps us driven and wanting. It provides anticipation and motivation. It pushes us into the uncomfortable to do what it takes to fulfil our desire. Dopamine is the driving force behind our obsession with achieving goals.

But the wanting makes us miserable. No matter how many hits we get, we will always be craving more. As Lieberman and Long point out, dopamine is never satisfied. No matter how many A's you get in school, how many cars you buy, how many pieces of your art you sell, or how strong your warrior pose becomes, dopamine will have you going from one accomplishment to another without ever feeling like you have arrived (Lieberman and Long 2018, 2–19).

Social scientist Arthur Brooks writes about an encounter that illustrates this. Years ago, on a red-eye flight from Los Angeles to Washington, DC, he overheard a conversation in the darkened cabin. The woman behind him was consoling her husband. Brooks couldn't understand much of what the distraught man was mumbling, but he could hear the wife's side of the conversation loud and clear. She was saying things like, "It's not *true* that no one needs you anymore. Oh, stop saying it would be better if you were dead."

The plane neared its destination. As the tray tables were stowed and lights illuminated the area, Brooks got a glimpse of the elderly couple seated behind him. He realized—much to his surprise—that the man was famous. This was someone with more accomplishments than most people, a "universally beloved" figure. As the passengers disembarked, even the captain of the plane gushed over the famous person, taking the opportunity to tell the man he had admired him ever since he was a little boy (Brooks 2022, xi–xii).

No one is immune from the dissatisfaction that plagues us. The anticipation of grasping that hard-to-reach carrot has us drooling over the possibility of finally arriving at "enough." But that destination—thanks to dopamine—is only an illusion.

How Stress Sabotages Goals

The problem is not just that goals generate stress, but that stress often sabotages goals. It's a negative feedback loop.

When we find ourselves with too much stress, we get poor sleep, become prone to mood swings, feel unable to prioritize, and have trouble making decisions—all while alienating people who might otherwise be helpful allies.

The compulsion to numb our uncomfortable feelings leads to procrastination, apathy, or any number of escapism behaviors, such as excessive shopping, gambling, drinking, or mindless scrolling on our phones. We develop tunnel vision, which can cloud the big picture, making problem-solving elusive. Our thinking becomes rigid. Our creativity and intuition feel blocked. Impulsivity and reactivity replace contemplation and thoughtful responding. We focus on individual self-preservation, and our collaborative abilities become strained. We begin to feel alone.

Movement System activation alters our relationship to time—so we never have enough of it, and we're always feeling rushed. When we are in this state, time feels compressed. The perpetual deadline looms, and we sacrifice quality for quickness. Reaching the finish line becomes our new panicked objective. We lose touch with our purpose and no longer enjoy the journey. In this way, too much Movement System energy can sideline the feeling of success—even if you do attain your goal.

Unrelenting stress stifles forward progress and brings exhaustion, burnout, self-criticism, and often complete disconnection from others. It shunts blood flow away from our brain's frontal lobe, where rational thought processes occur, causing our actions to become irrational and self-sabotaging.

Imagine Your Goal on the Stress Quadrant

To feel the effects of the Stress Quadrant on your goals, try this exercise (adapted from similar exercises in Deb Dana's 2020 book, *Befriending Your Nervous System*):

Think about a goal you are struggling to reach. I am not talking about to-do list goals like finishing your taxes. Think about a big, challenging goal you're pushing yourself toward—something on the level of establishing a new career, decluttering your house, or writing a book (sigh). What is your "Resurrection Window"-sized ambition?

Now imagine you are in a state of heightened fight-or-flight—major jazz-hands territory. This is the land of "I should" and "I have to." How do you interact with your goal while in this pressurized state?

Perhaps, for example, you aim to have your own cupcake shop (everyone has that goal, right?). The hard-charging energy of the Movement System might cause you to argue with your business partner about getting onboard. It might also give you a sense of urgency that convinces you to pay more than you can afford for a storefront location.

Now, think about your own big goal and take a few minutes to jot down what it's like to work on it from that high altitude. How does your relationship to your goal feel when you are in this fearful and extremely uncomfortable fight-or-flight state?

Next, imagine your same goal but with freeze energy. This is the "I can't" zone. How might you behave towards your big goal when you feel immobilized, hopeless, and disconnected? In our cupcake shop, freeze energy may feel like total despair. It might cause you to close your doors when an employee fails to show up for a shift. You might give up and quit after one negative review.

How do you feel about your own big goal when you are in that frozen state? Slouch forward and let your shoulders collapse a little. How does that change your relationship with your goal? Take a moment to write down these thoughts as well.

Okay. Let's shake that off. Take a few slow breaths with long exhalations. Allow some of that sparkling feel-good stillness into your body. Open your shoulders, relax your jaw, and let yourself feel expansive. What thoughts come to mind in relation to your goal when you're in a social engagement state?

Operating from a state of relaxation changes the story of our cupcake shop: The difficult discussion with your partner generates collaboration and alliance rather than ill-will. You take time to find a good location that makes financial sense rather than jumping into a bad decision. Employee issues cause annoyance instead of paralysis, and a bad review might just bolster your resolve to make your cupcake shop even better instead of crushing your confidence.

Take a few minutes to describe your relationship with your own chosen goal when you come at it from a state of social engagement.

I hope this exercise can provide insight into how your location on the Stress Quadrant affects the realization of your big dreams.

Disarming Dissatisfaction

So, we have dopamine, which craves novelty, and we have a nervous system that prioritizes predictability. It's a tug-of-war with no winners—unless we change the game. The experience Arthur Brooks had on that flight catapulted his curiosity about the pervasiveness of human dissatisfaction. He ended up writing a book on the subject. In *From Strength to Strength*, Brooks shares some compelling imagery:

> It is as if we were on a moving treadmill; satisfaction from success lasts but an instant. We can't stop to enjoy it; if we do, we zip off the back of the treadmill and wipe out. So we run and run, hoping that next success, greater than the last, will bring the enduring satisfaction we crave. (2022, 21)

Sounds stressful, doesn't it? We all seem to be failing the treadmill test. Our approach to striving for our goals is leaving us bruised and injured. Yet being driven isn't the problem. In fact, a drive to learn and grow—what psychologists call "mastery motivation"—strengthens resilience.

During an online book club, Dr. Lindsay Gibson, psychologist and author of *Who You Were Meant to Be*, explained our drive to grow and find purpose is innate—no matter what age we are. It's what she calls a "human mandate." According to Dr. Gibson, "We have something in us that is trying to actualize itself." It is something that is "bigger than you," meaning it is outside of your conscious choice. Suppressing it leads to "feelings of frustration or depression or purposelessness or meaninglessness—because there really is something that wants you to become who you were meant to be" (Gibson 2023).

Is there a solution? A Settled Section for our goals, perhaps?

Indeed, there is. Goals don't have to push you over the edge. You can find your way to success without getting stuck in the fight-or-flight energy of overachieving or the freeze energy of giving up. You must find balance between the Movement System and the Stillness System. This, of course, also requires building the capacity to tolerate sitting with uncomfortable sensations. From a more regulated place, we can discern whether the uncomfortable sensations our goals are producing are dangerous or just unpleasant. How to go about doing that is the topic of our next chapter.

CHAPTER 23

Cartwheeling into Uncomfortable

Redefining the word "success" changes our relationship to goals, moving us from empty productivity to our full purpose. From what we know about chronic dissatisfaction in our society, the dictionary definition of success—"the achieving of the results wanted or hoped for"—seems limited (Cambridge 2023). Our hoped-for accomplishments don't necessarily bring a sense of success.

We need an alternative definition, and here's my version: *Success is feeling safe enough to play.*

It's an unorthodox definition, but it solved the success problem for me. Suddenly, wanting something no longer brought dissatisfaction and misery. This shift steers us away from seeking awards, approval, and accolades and guides us toward a true spirit of lightness and joy in our pursuits. When I am stuck in a stress response, victories don't even feel good. It takes a regulated nervous system to savor satisfaction. It takes feeling safe enough to play.

Using body-based regulation tools creates a sense of safety. It allows the mind-body to distinguish between what is a threat and what is just discomfort.

This is important because, as we discussed in Chapter 3, calm is not always appropriate; we need to have some of that uncomfortable fight-or-flight energy to reach a goal.

When we're striving for something, the alertness of the Movement System gives us the wind in our sails. But if that wind whips up and tosses us about, then tethering ourselves with safety and play stops the storm from making us feel like jumping overboard! Successful achievement of a goal requires us to manage the stress responses the goal itself creates.

The mother of all goals is a settled nervous system. From the Settled Section we can balance both arousal energy and groundedness to stay the course towards our aspirations. By distinguishing discomfort from true danger, regulation increases our capacity to hold the uncomfortable and still move forward.

Once we have that energized-calm feeling in our bodies, play can help us maintain our sense of safety because you can't play *and* be in emergency mode at the same time. Besides, play also brings fun!

My Kind of Play

One beautiful Sunday afternoon, I headed to the Huntington Library and Botanical Gardens in San Marino, California, to have a "writing play date" with my book—the very book you are reading!

The sprawling 120-acre property was busy with visitors to its many gardens and art collections, and I was lucky to find a parking spot in section B1 (remember that, please, so I can find my car on the way out). It had been years since I'd been to the Huntington. We used to come regularly when my son was in a stroller, and the koi ponds and children's fountains would keep him happy (and wet) for hours.

The place had changed since I last saw it—sometime between our membership lapsing and our son growing facial hair. A new welcome desk greeted me at the entrance along with a new café.

I maneuvered around a crowd near the library and made a beeline for the gardens. But as I strode along the path, I could feel that familiar need to rush. Even though I was in an ideal place for peaceful meandering, I was hurrying as if I were late to a big meeting.

I decided to stop at a bench nestled under a shady tree. As soon as I sat down, I took a slow, deep breath. For the next five minutes (or maybe it was twenty), I didn't focus on my book or anything else. I just sat, watching people stroll by.

At some point, I realized my polaroid-perfect perch was in the Camellia Garden. I noticed the white, pink, and red petals flanking the area. Then their aroma finally hit my nose. My senses were tickled; I knew this was a clue that I was beginning to relax.

I let my mind wander. When I am at ease, ideas come to me, and I found myself jotting down little epiphanies.

The playfulness I was feeling gave me energy and a strong urge to move. And yet I was relaxed. My body was telling me to get up and go see more, while at the same time, telling me to stay seated and enjoy more. I was straddling two states—alertness and stillness.

That is what play is after all: a mix of uncomfortable and comfortable, elevated energy yet grounded calm. It is an odd-but-wonderful paradox to hold. And it gave me both the energy to focus on manuscript ideas and the carefree headspace to receive new creative input.

This "date" was straight out of Julia Cameron's book *The Artist's Way*. Cameron suggests putting weekly "artist dates" on your calendar and using them to nurture "your creative consciousness." The goal of an artist date, she says, is to receive, "opening yourself to insight, inspiration, guidance" (2016, 18–23).

The Science of Play

We found it natural to play in childhood, but it's important to embrace play in adulthood, too. When we play, the brain releases natural opioids, encouraging the prefrontal cortex to be open to new options, further possibilities, and—in my case—evoke more book ideas. These "feel-good" opioids combine with small doses of adrenaline from the Movement System to give play its paradoxical relaxed-yet-energized state (Siviy and Panksepp 2011).

Dr. Stuart Brown calls play a "survival drive" necessary for developing social skills, flexible learning, and problem solving. He recommends tapping into early childhood memories of times when you felt engaged and joyful, which can guide you as you're finding your version of play as an adult (Brown 2015).

Play can also help you recover from childhood experiences in which play was forcibly suppressed or stripped of its enjoyment. If a bully ridiculed your kindergarten scribbles or overprotective parents restricted your explorations, it may be particularly important for you to reclaim your freedom to play.

Dr. Brown emphasizes the need for this reclaiming:

> Whenever the unique, intrinsic motivation of the child is not honored and the child is lock-stepped into a performance to please the adult ambition model, something very precious and authentic for that child's future is lost... or at least needs to be recovered later. (Brown 2015)

When I was growing up, dance was my favorite form of play. So, as an adult, for one of my weekly "play dates," I danced around my living room to Prince songs. I wasn't thinking about my book—just moving my body, swaying my hips, and immersing myself in the rhythm of the music.

On another "date" I played with artistic creativity using a combination of collage and abstract painting. I'm not much of a visual artist, but I find creating with my hands to be a gateway to my calming nervous system. Doing art for art's sake—not seeking accolades or comparing myself to others—is freeing and playful. Psychotherapist Stefanie Milner adds, "When making art with free creative reign and no pressure from others or the need to be good at what they are creating, many find that the process of creating something (anything!) builds confidence."

Sure enough, when I returned to the task of writing, my self-critical mind had quieted, and my confidence felt boosted.

Tim Carey, the stained-glass artist you met in the last chapter, couldn't turn to art as play during his stressful undertaking since his artistry was both the goal *and* the source of his stress.

Instead, when the "Resurrection Window" project became too much (right around the time he needed to create the face of Christ), Tim took a week-long fishing trip with his father and brothers. He followed up with another form of play: coaching his son's Little League baseball team.

Former workaholic Charlie Hoehn writes about his recovery from anxiety and overworking in *Play It Away.* During a desperate time of exhaustion, failing health, and emotional instability, Hoehn found relief in various types of play, including improvisational theatre:

> Improv wasn't about keeping score, or self-improvement, or even acting funny. It was about being in the moment and letting go. And for a few glorious hours, I didn't need to be my anxious, workaholic, perfectionist self. I could just play around and have guilt-free fun. (2014, 35)

Remember Adam Grant and his languishing from Chapter 3? In an episode of *The Happiness Lab* podcast, Grant describes the benefits of losing himself in weekly Mario Kart tournaments with his family. He would jump around throwing virtual turtles at a six-year-old on-screen opponent—yelling, feeling challenged, and having a blast. Grant pulled himself onto more neutral neural ground through that adrenaline-producing thing called play (Santos 2022).

Connection to Something Bigger

Tethering yourself to spirituality is another way to feel safe when goals become too uncomfortable.

I asked Carey what he would do, in retrospect, if he ever again faced a stress as massive as his window project. He told me he would visit the ocean more.

I, too, am partial to the ocean when I'm stressed out. For both of us, the ocean provides a sense of awe and wonder—a feeling of connection to something bigger than ourselves. With the ocean, you suddenly feel a oneness with the universe instead of assuming it all revolves around you.

Dacher Keltner, author of *Awe: The New Science of Everyday Wonder and How It Can Transform Your Life*, defines "awe" as "the feeling of being in the presence of something vast that transcends your current understanding of the world" (2023, 7). Researcher Dr. Lisa Miller poetically described it as "moving from a point to a wave." In her book, *The Awakened Brain*, Miller writes about an important discovery she and her lab made about spirituality: "[h]ighly spiritual brains are thicker and stronger in *exactly the same regions* that weaken and wither in depressed brains" (2021, 7 and 157). Spirituality, whether religious or secular, appears to protect our emotional wellbeing.

Whether your spirituality involves a divine god or other mystical forces doesn't matter—only that you experience a sense of marvel and bewilderment.

Much like Carey's, my spirituality is intertwined with nature. Several times during the writing of this book, I felt a magnetic draw towards scenic, outdoor vistas. I made visits to the desert, had many beach getaways, and enjoyed a mountain retreat. All were sacred places to stir my creativity, places where incessant overprotective thoughts around failure, insecurity, and self-criticism quieted to an incomprehensible whisper.

I am not religious, but I do consider myself to be spiritual. I believe I have guardian angels watching over me, and I look for serendipities, coincidences, synchronicities (whatever you want to call them) as signs of their guidance and direction.

The impetus to write this book came from a series of curious serendipities.

During a holiday get-together, my friend Jill said matter-of-factly, "You should write a book, Chantal." She was either tired of my annoying habit of giving everyone—friend or stranger—advice on how to manage their stress, or she really felt I had good information to offer. In any case, the conversation left me tickled. I didn't think much of it, though, until later that evening when I told my husband about the conversation with Jill. "You *should* write a book," he agreed. "In fact, it is already under the tree."

"What is under the tree?" I asked.

He wasn't too happy his surprise had been spoiled, but he said, "I created a 'writer's retreat' for you and got you two nights at an Airbnb. All by yourself. So you can write."

The next day I met my friend Deanna for lunch at a cute outdoor café. I'll never forget the two of us sitting across from each other, Cobb salads at the ready, and Deanna saying, "I signed up for this course where they teach you how to write a book. The program starts in two months."

I stopped picking at my bacon and stared at her. Time stood still. A wave of warm shivers passed through me, and I blurted out, "Yes. Sign me up." There was no brain chatter, no weighing of pros and cons, no protecting myself against a big, scary challenge. It was a decisive, calm, expansive, and confident reply to the universe telling me: "Here is a path for you to follow."

Anchoring in a connection to the unknown, the spirit world, or the divine (whatever that means to you), keeps you from spinning and crashing as you pursue your goals. Look for the signs. Revel in the awe of the universe. Let it bring some stillness to your Movement System.

Mindset Revisited

Remember Dr. Alia Crum's stress mindset theory from Chapter 4? This is the idea that we can sculpt our perception of stress to reap its benefits. One place where tapping into the power of the mind can mitigate stress is with goals.

Shifting your stress mindset is *not* about giving yourself a pep talk. This isn't an "I've got this!" approach. Nor is it about convincing yourself your stressors are "good." Orienting to a challenge stress mindset is about viewing your stress as enhancing—vital to your forward momentum. You embrace the stress because, even when difficult, you believe it can help.

We talked about how this concept can be misused to dismiss certain stressors—often systemic injustices. If your goal is to move up the corporate ladder and your career advancement is being blocked because of discrimination, physical disability, or chronic illness, then mindset isn't going to help (but hopefully your HR department will). When it comes to these problems, no amount of mindset reframing could convince your body you are safe. In such cases, it is best to start with body-based regulation tools.

If, on the other hand, you are stressed out because reaching for the stars has increased your challenges or responsibilities, cognitive reappraisal can be a powerful tool. Perhaps you are renovating your home, upgrading your website, or preparing to give a speech. Or perhaps you want to bring your business ideas and opinions to the leadership table. These are the types of situations where relabeling your stress as "enhancing" is most fitting and effective. Re-directing your perception of stress works best on what Crum calls "goal-directed efforts" (Huberman 2022). When your stress is chosen and purposeful, think of Movement System energy as providing stepping stones for growth, learning, performance, focus, and wellbeing.

Avoiding the Stress Extremes

Play, spirituality, and mindset theory are all powerful tools for settling your nervous system when stress threatens your pursuit of your dreams. If you are stress-sensitive like me, these tools can help secure your footing so goals happen in the Settled Section.

Instead of trying to keep up with the Kardashians, we can now center our ambitions on our intrinsic purpose. This way, when we do succeed, we can enjoy our achievements in a deeper, more satisfying way. We can get off the treadmill—or at least, we can slow down and enjoy the ride.

Step Nine:

Don't Stress About De-stressing

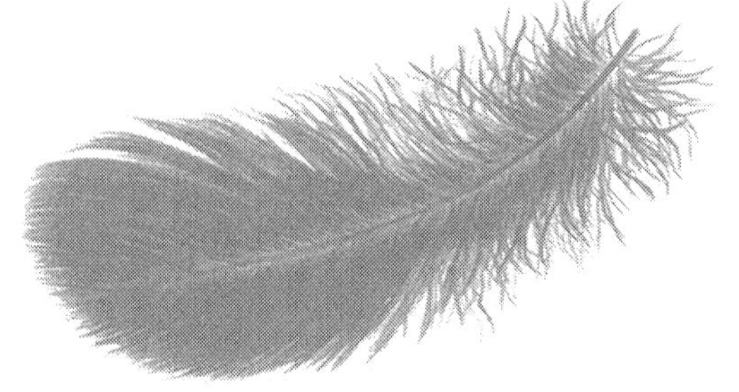

CHAPTER 24

Final(ly) Thoughts

And speaking of reaching goals...

Ta-da! We made it to the finish line. If you are reading this, it means I completed my goal of publishing a book.

In the past, I never would have attempted to *outline* a book, let alone write one. The stress of it would have been my undoing. And yet, here we are, my friends, at the end of the journey. Or perhaps, more accurately, the end of the book and the continuation of the journey. Let's face it, exploring our relationship to stress and learning to communicate with our bodies are part of a never-ending odyssey.

Throughout the writing process, I *mostly* avoided the stress rollercoaster I would have historically been riding during such an endeavor. That is not to say I wasn't stressed out. I was. Ask my husband, my son, and my friends! I had occasional freak-outs, tantrums, meltdowns, tension headaches, crying fits, and at least a couple (okay, five!) proclamations of quitting. But the ideas and tools I've shared with you in this book anchored me during those ups and downs. The rollercoaster climbs were less steep, the drops less precipitous, and the ride more moderate and tranquil. The tools allowed me to notice if my stress responses were appropriate. They gave me the opportunity to reset and recommit to my mission. Time and again, they returned me to the typewriter (okay, keyboard).

The tools in this book can settle you too, particularly when your alarm system has gotten stuck or become overly sensitive. You are not expected to always be calm, though. That is not the goal. And when you are over-responding, you may not be able to settle your nervous system. That's okay too. You are human, after all—not a robot.

No matter what coping strategies you've used in the past, know they were adaptive. Whether you shut down, escaped, or numbed, your body-mind did what was necessary to help you in the moment. Now that you have a better understanding of stress responses and how humans get stuck, you will be able to spend more time in your Settled Section and less time in survival mode. The compulsion to shut down, escape, or numb will become less frequent. When it does happen, it will be less compulsive, more conscious, and shorter in duration. These are signs of progress and healing.

This transition won't happen overnight. The shift will be incremental. When I started using body-based regulation tools, it took several months before I noticed a change in myself. Slowly, my "window of tolerance" widened. I gained a greater ability to recognize what was overwhelming to me versus what was just uncomfortable—and to respond accordingly.

Instead of flinging myself into the far reaches of frantic or freeze, the Settled Section became my home.

The Mind

Once I was in a more settled place, I could bring in more mind-based tools. I could examine and alter the prediction patterns of my brain, bringing them into closer alignment with present circumstances. No longer was my mind confusing something in the present with stories from my past, sending my inner alarm system into hyperdrive.

When I talk about the mind, I'm referring to our thoughts. Many people describe this inner aspect of ourselves using the concept of the ego. We often hear about the ego in negative terms, as a judgmental "inner critic" or a chatterbox "monkey-mind." We are taught to ignore or transcend our thoughts—to see them as a source of distraction or a bothersome impediment that we must control if we are to escape their hold on us.

Negative thoughts and feelings, I was taught, are from that overbearing ego: the saboteur, the trickster, the bully. For the longest time, I had trouble accepting that somewhere inside my cranium is an enemy trying to sabotage my life. What purpose did such a troublemaker serve?

Internal Family Systems

When I came across Internal Family Systems (IFS), things shifted for me. This theory, developed by psychologist Dr. Richard Schwartz, flips the ego-as-hinderance idea upside down. In his book, *No Bad Parts*,

Schwartz suggests we do not have one mind, but rather multiple "parts" existing within everyone. We all have a true (capital "S") Self, defined as "an essence of calm, clarity, compassion, and connectedness" (Schwartz 2021, 1).

What I love most about the IFS approach is that our egos (or in Schwartz's vernacular, our "parts") are protectors. They are "simply trying to keep us safe and are reacting to and containing other parts that carry emotions and memories from past traumas we have locked away inside" (Schwartz 2021, 13).

When Schwartz helps patients get to know their underlying parts, they discover this protectiveness developed because a part is stuck in the past. In this way, IFS is the perfect complement to our compassionate understanding of stress responses. Schwartz examines the mind in the same way we examined the body and its reactions to stress—without vilification. In each case, it is a nurturing, self-compassionate philosophy that guides us.

Over the years, I have tried to stop my negative thoughts and talk myself out of being stressed. Those tactics never helped in any permanent or even long-term way. Once my body felt livable, though, I could then focus on my thinking. Settling my body was foundational in settling my mind; IFS added to that solid infrastructure, encouraging my mind and helping it along.

Settled into We

My personal metamorphosis—my experience with the work I've shared with you here—has been nothing short of profound. I am changed.

I hope I have provided you with enough breadcrumbs to start a similar journey—that there were "aha" moments leading to more "ahhhh" moments in your life. More than that, my biggest, truest desire is that the information and tools support you and allow you to move through this world in a way that's connected, compassionate, and loving—towards yourself and everyone around you. With collective effort—one settled nervous system to another—we can heal, grow, and thrive *together.* Joseph Campbell once said, "Survival is the second law of life. The first is that we are all one." And with that nugget of wisdom, I will leave you, my friends, and I will say *bonne nuit.*

CHAPTER 25

The Settlement (Summary of Tools)

We have built a strong foundation together. You now know how to identify your stress responses using your soul speak (i.e., interoception) as your main guide. You are beginning a new relationship with stress—one with a more curious and compassionate quality.

This chapter provides a recap and easy reference of the settling tools shared throughout this book. What follows are the basic instructions for each tool. For more details about a tool, please refer back to the original chapter containing the full description.

As with any wellness program, the focus on making things better may cause stress. You may feel like pushing yourself to make changes—a sense of urgency towards resetting your alarm system. That urgency runs counter to what your nervous system needs and wants. Pushing will trigger more alarm, not less. Instead, it is best to approach these tools with slowness, gentleness, and patience. The goal is to convey safety to your system.

Go easy on yourself. Don't stress about de-stressing.

Before Opening Your Toolkit

As you incorporate these exercises and techniques into your daily life, please remember these four things:

1. Not all the tools will work for you. You need to play detective to figure out which assortment works best for you and under which circumstances. This will take time and practice. If a tool is making you feel worse, please don't keep using it. Try another one. You'd be surprised how many people get anxious using breathing techniques, while others feel invincible afterwards. Everybody is different, and every body is different.
2. Start small. Add tools incrementally. Some people prefer to pick a tool and do a short version of it around the same time each day. For example, maybe every morning after you brush your teeth, you check in with how you're feeling, and you practice the physiological sigh (double inhale, long exhale). And maybe that is all you do for the first two weeks before trying another tool.
3. You can use tools in the middle of a stressful episode (real-time tools) or in daily practice. Using tools daily tends to increase the likelihood that you will turn to them when you're in a state of stress. I recommend being consistent with your daily practice. However, don't beat yourself up if you skip a week or your practice drops off. When developing a new habit, relapsing back into old habits is part of the process and should be expected. It's not that it *might* happen; it *will* happen. Knowing this is so liberating! It frees us from self-defeating

patterns of shame and shutdown, which come from giving relapses unjustified power over us.

4. Tools can be used for any situation. If I shared a tool in the chapter "Eat," for example, you can still use that tool in other situations besides eating. You can use your favorite tools any time, under any stressful circumstance, or to address any stress symptom: insomnia, pain, addictive behaviors, compulsive behaviors, negative mood, menopause symptoms, digestive problems (constipation, diarrhea, or IBS), fatigue, weak immune system, lack of libido, concentration issues, poor memory, etc.

The Resilience Toolkit Guiding Questions

1. What is my stress state? Where am I on the Stress Quadrant?
2. How do I know?
3. Is my stress helpful to me at this moment?
4. If my stress is not helpful, what can I do to lower my stress?
5. How do I know the practice successfully lowered my stress?

List of Tools

Here is the QR Code with links to the videos of all the settling tools.

Breathe

Rotation Reset

1. Stand with your feet hip width apart.
2. Bend your knees slightly and keep them bent throughout the exercise.
3. With your arms hanging loosely by your side, begin to slowly rotate your torso from right to left. Your arms should swing freely.
4. Let your head follow the movement, looking from left to right, left to right.
5. Allow your arms to wrap around your lower abdomen and back as they swing.

Repeat as many times as you like. Ten times is usually a good amount of reps, but there is no magic number.

Ribcage Reeducation

Sitting or standing in front of a mirror (be sure you can see yourself from the waist up), fold a bath towel lengthwise and wrap it around your lower ribcage.

1. Grab the edges of the towel by crossing your arms in front of you so the left hand grabs the end of the towel on your right side and the right hand grabs the towel on the left.
2. Now pull your hands closer together so that the towel becomes more snug around your body.
3. Relax your shoulders.
4. As you inhale, focus on pushing your ribcage into the towel. As you exhale, allow the towel to

encourage the ribs to close by gently drawing in tighter around your torso.

5. Try to keep the neck as relaxed as possible, and your collarbones down rather than elevated.

Sitz-Bones Walk Back

1. From a seated position, put your hands under your buttocks and find your "sits bones" (the bones sticking out at the base of your pelvis).
2. Once you have found them, "walk" one side back and then the other, towards the back of your chair. This should increase the natural arch in the small of your back.
3. Be sure your ribcage is not jutting forward but is in line with your pelvis.

Up Breathing

Right Nostril Breathing (to increase energy and alertness)

1. Using your finger, block your left nostril.
2. Inhale and exhale three to ten times through the right side of your nose.

Down Breathing

Left Nostril Breathing (to decrease anxiety or tension)

1. Using your finger, block your right nostril.
2. Inhale and exhale three to ten times through the left side of your nose.

Long Exhalation Breathing

1. Inhale for a slow count of four and exhale for a slow count of six.
2. Repeat three to ten times.

Alternate version: Inhale for a slow count of three and exhale for a slow count of six.

Physiological Sigh

1. Take two short, back-to-back inhalations through your nose.
2. Follow by a long exhale through your mouth.

Move

Gentle Movement Options
Progressive Tension/Relaxation

1. Lying comfortably on your back, start by squeezing your toes and then releasing them.
2. Slowly work your way up your body, one muscle group at a time, tensing and releasing. Toes, feet, front of the leg, abdominals... back, chest, arms, face.

Rag-Doll Shake

1. Fold in half at your waist, as if you are trying to touch your toes.
2. Keep a soft bend in your knees.
3. From this position, shake your arms and legs for approximately thirty seconds before slowly rolling up to a standing position.

Modification: If you have back pain, this exercise should be done standing upright.

Core Work

Option 1

Weight Shift: Shift your weight back to your heels while standing.

Option 2

Laugh: Try going to a comedy club, watching a funny movie, or spending time with some hilarious friends.

Option 3

Stork Stance: Bend your left leg and don't let it touch your right leg. Hold that single leg stance on your right leg for as long as you can—up to thirty seconds. Once you can stand on one leg without losing your balance, to make this more challenging add slow head turns to the right and left while in stork stance.

Stretch

Scalene Stretch (right side)

1. Bring your left ear towards your left shoulder.
2. Maintaining the side-bent position, tilt your head up slightly so you are looking up to the ceiling.
3. Hold that position for thirty seconds, being sure to breathe from your lower ribcage area.
4. Repeat the same thing on the other side.

Psoas Release Using a Massage Ball (right side)

1. Place your right index finger on the front of your pelvic bone.

2. Place your left index finger on your bellybutton.
3. Draw an imaginary diagonal line between your two fingers.
4. The center of this line is where you will place your massage ball.
5. Keeping the ball at the center of the diagonal line, lie on your stomach and relax over the ball.
6. Stay in that relaxed position for a minute or two or until you feel a softening in the muscle.
7. Repeat on the left side.

SCM Stretch (right side)

1. Bend your head to the left side (left ear towards left shoulder).
2. Keep that side-bent position and rotate your head to the left.
3. Maintain that position and tilt your head back slightly. Feel the stretch on the right side.
4. Hold for thirty seconds, breathing slowly from your lower ribcage or diaphragm.
5. Repeat on the other side.

Upper Trapezius Muscle Stretch (right side)

1. Sit or stand up tall and place your right arm with your elbow bent behind you, resting it in the small of your back.
2. Slowly, side bend your head to the left. In other words, bring your left ear towards your left shoulder without moving your body—just move your head.
3. Hold for thirty seconds then repeat on the other side.

Eat

Mindful Eating

1. Slow down. Don't rush your meal.
2. Take in your food visually—notice the colors and shapes on your plate.
3. Smell the aroma of your food. As you eat, pay attention to the texture and temperature. As you chew, notice if the flavors change over time.

Alternating Side-Eye

1. While lying on your back, sitting, or standing, interlace your fingers together and place your hands behind your head.
2. Allow your hands to rest at the base of your skull with the heel of each hand resting on the bone just behind each ear.
3. Keeping your head straight forward (not turned to the right or left), shift your gaze so that you are looking towards your left elbow.
4. Hold that eye position for approximately thirty seconds or until you feel a sign of calming.
5. Bring your gaze back to center.
6. Look in the direction of your right elbow.
7. Hold for thirty seconds or until you get a signal that you relaxed a little.

Jaw Release

1. Lightly place your fingertips on either side of your jaw, just in front your ears. Open and close your mouth a few times. You will feel movement under your hands if you are in the correct position.

2. Let your tongue rest on the roof of your closed mouth.
3. With your fingertips on each side, slowly massage your jaw, using a gentle, circular motion.
4. After four or five little circles, glide your hands down slightly following the jawline and massage there for a while.
5. Continue rubbing in a circular motion as you follow your jawbone along the bottom of your face all the way to your chin.

You can repeat this process a few times if you like. You do not need a lot of pressure.

For a more advanced version, jut your lower jaw forward *slightly* as you perform this self-massage.

Sense

Finding Your Sensory Superpower

1. For five consecutive days, pick one sensory experience (taste, touch, vision, sound, or smell) to focus on.
2. Each day, rotate to a new sense.
3. As you go about your daily activities, work on being more cognizant of the "sense of the day."

Orient

Turning your head slowly to the left and right as you take in your environment.

Panoramic Vision

1. Without moving your head or eyes, take in as much of your *distant* visual field—above, below, and on the sides—as possible.
2. Feel your eyes soften, almost as if they are relaxing farther back into your skull.

SCM Massage (right side)

1. Rotate your head to the left. On the right side of the neck, the muscle will pop out. It is a tight band running from just behind the ear to the sternum and collarbone.
2. Using a light touch, place your fingers just behind the base of your ears.
3. Gently sweep them straight down along the tight band-like muscle on the right.
4. Follow that band down to your right collarbone.
5. Repeat five to ten times, sweeping from behind the ear to the upper shelf of the sternum and collarbone.
6. Pay attention to how that massage technique registers in your body.
7. Repeat on the left side of the neck.

Note: You can also choose to gently pinch the SCM to release it. When you turn your head, gently use your thumb and index fingers to pinch the band-like muscle from just below the ear down to the collarbone.

Plantar Fascia Foot Rolling

1. While standing or sitting, place a small ball on the floor and then rest your foot on the ball.
2. Roll the ball around the arch of the foot, moving slowly towards the toes. Repeat on the other foot.

Parenting

Vagal Toning

Hum, sing, or gargle (cold water works best).

How to Bee-Breathe:

1. Sitting comfortably, place your thumbs in your ears and your fingers over your closed eyes. Alternatively, your hands can rest in your lap.
2. Keeping your mouth closed, inhale through your nose.
3. As you exhale through your nose, make a humming sound in the back of your throat. Exhale for as long as possible without straining.
4. Repeat as many times as you like, usually three to ten times.

Improving Relationships

Barometer or Brat

1. Excuse yourself from the interaction so you can be alone.
2. Check in with yourself: Where are you on the Stress Quadrant? Where were you before the incident? If appropriate, try a quick settling tool.

3. Once you have noted a little settling within your system, consider the following questions: Do you still feel as offended, irritated, or enraged? When you think about the other person's actions, words, or point of view, do you now have more understanding or less?

***During* a stressful situation:**

- Slow your movement and breath down.
- Try expanding your vision (panoramic vision).
- Try entrainment breathing.
- Lower the pitch of your voice.

The Art of Rushing

Alternating Squeezes

1. You can be sitting or standing for this exercise. Start by using your right hand to gently squeeze your left arm just below the shoulder. Hold this squeeze for a couple of seconds. Don't forget to keep breathing.
2. Move your right hand down a couple of inches so it's just above your left elbow and squeeze again. Hold that squeeze for a second or two.
3. Move it down again to just above the wrist—you can bend your elbow if you wish. Squeeze and hold, being sure not to hold your breath.
4. Repeat the entire sequence on the opposite side, with your left hand squeezing your right arm.

Resources

Soul Speak

The Resilience Toolkit is part of Lumos Transforms.

https://lumostransforms.com/intro-to-the-resilience-toolkit/ or https://theresiliencetoolkit.co/event-calendar/

Chronic Pain

If you or a loved one has chronic pain and you would like more information on how pain works, visit the Noigroup for helpful resources:

https://www.noigroup.com/

Amari Dior at Body Amor Wellness Chronic Pain Coaching

https://www.bodyamorwellness.com/

Stretch

Psoas self-massage ball options:

Yamuna Body Ball. The standard size (Gold) is perfect for most muscles including the hip flexors.

https://www.yamunausa.com/collections/balls-and-essentials/products/gold-ball?variant=689811007

Tune Up Fitness Coregeous Ball. This one is perfect for most muscles, including the hip flexors.

https://www.tuneupfitness.com/shop/massage-balls/coregeous-ball

Eat

Deprogram Diet Culture online program by Dr. Supatra Tovar

https://anew-insight.com/deprogram-diet-culture/

Sense

Trauma Geek, Janae Elisabeth

https://www.traumageek.com

https://www.facebook.com/TraumaGeek/

Broken Connections

For a deeper dive into a body-based perspective on racism, please read Resmaa Menakem's *My Grandmother's Hands: Racialized Trauma and the Pathway to Mending Our Hearts and Bodies.*

Menakem's website is also a good resource for further learning: https://www.resmaa.com/

Parenting

Joanna Clark at Blissful Baby Sleep Coaching
https://www.blissfulbabysleepcoaching.com
https://www.instagram.com/blissfulbabysleep/

Improving Relationships

One Love Foundation - Help people identify and safely leave abusive relationships.
https://www.joinonelove.org

Pushing into Uncomfortable

Holy Frit Movie

As of the writing of this book, *Holy Frit* is working on distribution. Please go to https://holyfrit.com/ to find out where you can watch this fascinating and entertaining documentary.

Acknowledgments

You can't get by on the savanna or the city streets without others, and you certainly can't write a book alone.

I'd like to thank my tribe of people who guided, supported, and cheered me on through this epic pilgrimage:

My editors at New Degree Press (NDP), thank you to:

Angela Mitchell, for helping me develop my voice before I knew I had one.

Mary Ann Tate, who practically carried me over the first-draft finish line. You are so good at coaxing the best out of me, and I will be forever grateful.

Jordana Megonigal, for your structural suggestions that changed the flow of the book for the better.

Christina Sng, whose sweet demeanor, praise, and talent with a red pen sharpened and honed the book's message. I wouldn't have hung on till the end without your talents and plaudits keeping me going. I always felt like I had someone watching out for me (and monitoring my overuse of the word "that").

Michelle Felich, for your stellar copy-editing skills and heartfelt praise.

Thank you to my main editor (outside of NDP), **Katie Scrivner**. You made the book so much better. You made me easier to read and helped my words flow more effortlessly. Your tireless, unwavering, and *calm* patience with me and my crazy changes, additions, subtractions, and re-writes is a testament to your exceptional soul. And I love that your last name is so befitting your prowess as a grammar, punctuation, and overall amazing scribe. You are a ninja with words, and I am so lucky you joined me on this adventure.

To **Kristy Carter** at NDP, thank you for saving me when I "lost" an entire chapter somewhere in an internet black hole.

Jacques Moolman at NDP, thank you for your encouragement and advice. You helped me realize that marketing and self-promotion don't have to make me feel so shallow. Still working on that.

To all the people I interviewed, **Shola Richards, Janae Elisabeth, Arrowyn Ambrose, Joanna Clark, Jill Miller, Amari Dior, Karen Osborne, Michelle Babb, Justin Monroe, Tim Carey, Dr. Supatra Tovar, Dr. Miriam Zylberglait, Aunt Sue**, as well as everyone whose identities I did not reveal (you know who you are)—thank you for your generous time and for sharing your stories.

To my beta readers who read one, two, and sometimes four early versions of chapters and gave me constructive feedback, you are all so appreciated. Your comments helped shape this book into a more relatable experience for a wider swath of people and perspectives:

Heather Bland
Deanna Moffitt
Dr. Saul Levine
Dr. Ruby Kalra
Dr. Miriam Zylberglait
Julia Albert Olsson
The Husband
Louise Pitot
Pam Aschbacher
Bill Buckley
Jill Brenek
Emily Cline
Robert McLaughlin
Cindie Zumberge
Arrowyn Ambrose
Diane Plitka-Kozak

Special beta reader thanks to **Dr. Supatra Tovar, Laura Horn, Stefanie Schamber, Deborah Bouis, and Libby Hinsley** who all gave their time and expertise to assist in making me look smarter.

For her help with early research, thank you to **Sara Moerlein Donnelly**. I got lucky in the sister-in-law department.

Ianthe Zevos, for being the kind of friend who starts out agreeing to meet for coffee to chat about design advice and ends up spearheading book cover ideas. You are a true friend in every sense of the word. So grateful you are in my life.

Deb Schwartz, for her artistic guidance.

Gala Slater and Clare Walsh, for their beautiful cover design.

Karie Reynolds, for being so generous with her marketing savvy.

Kirstine Ortega, for her assistance in keeping my head on straight and my graphics and social media on track.

Danny Brown, for his way with a camera and helping me feel relaxed in front of it.

Dr. Lindsay Gibson, for her mentorship as a fellow author. Your guidance helped me embrace the scary word "author" with more grace and confidence.

To my Operation Springtime posse (**Emily Cline** and **Jill Brenek**)—I wouldn't have pursued my interest in stress management were it not for your gentle nudges. The check-ins, the words of reassurance, this book was carried on the shoulders of your friendship and support.

Deanna Moffitt, thank you for letting me tag along with you when you said you were writing a book. And for our multiple writing sessions together. Your flattering enjoyment of my writing style coupled with your honesty when it wasn't working was the perfect tonic for my growth as an author.

I owe a lot of what I know about stress and trauma to **Nkem Ndefo**. I am so grateful for your knowledge and ability to relay important information in an engaging, compassionate manner. Thank you for creating the Resilience Toolkit Certification Program, along with the guiding questions, and for allowing me to share them with a shell-shocked world. You are a remarkable catalyst for positive change.

Thank you to **my patients**—it's a cliché, but it's true: you are my teachers.

Mom and Dad—thank you for your unconditional love and support throughout my ups and downs on the rollercoaster. No matter where I am on the Stress Quadrant, you are always there for me. I was born with the golden ticket! I love you both very much.

Aidan Donnelly, thank you for putting up with your mom's bonkers goal of writing a book and your patience with me as I navigate being a better, more regulated mother. Watching you grow into the incredible man you are today is one of the greatest joys of my life.

Ed Donnelly, there are no words, my love. The way you encourage and protect and bolster me—only carrying me when I really need it—makes me grateful I married you every. single. day. From debating the respectability of using the word "overwhelm" as a noun to listening to me complain about my deadline, to making me dinner so I could keep typing away, you were always my best sounding board and my best friend on this journey. Thank you for being my soulmate.

Appendix

The Settled Section

Siegel, Daniel J. 2020. *The Developing Mind: How Relationships and the Brain Interact to Shape Who We Are.* Read by Fred Stella. Grand Haven, MI: Brilliance Audio. Audible audio ed., 31 hrs., 40 min.

The Stress Quadrant

Holmes, Thomas H., and Richard H. Rahe. 1967. "The Social Readjustment Rating Scale." *Journal of Psychosomatic Research* 11, no. 2 (August): 213–218. https://doi.org/10.1016/0022-3999(67)90010-4.

Porges, Stephen W. 2017. *The Pocket Guide to the Polyvagal Theory: The Transformative Power of Feeling Safe*. New York: W.W. Norton & Company.

Calm Isn't Always the Goal

Byrd-Craven, Jennifer, Brandon Auer, and Shiela Kennison. 2015. "Sex differences in salivary cortisol responses to sex-linked stressors: A test of the Tend-and-Befriend Model." *Adaptive Human Behavior and Physiology* 1, no. 4: 408–420. https://doi.org/10.1007/s40750-014-0013-1.

Grant, Adam. 2021. "There's a Name for the Blah You're Feeling: It's Called Languishing." *New York Times*, April 29, 2021. https://www.nytimes.com/2021/04/19/well/mind/covid-mental-health-languishing.html.

Juster, Robert-Paul, Mark L. Hatzenbuehler, Adrianna Mendrek, James G. Pfaus, Nathan Grant Smith, Philip Jai Johnson, Jean-Philippe Lefebvre-Louis, Catherine Raymond, Marie-France Marin, Shireen Sindi, Sonia J. Lupien, and Jens C. Pruessner. 2015. "Sexual Orientation and Stress Reactivity." *Biological Psychiatry* 77, no. 7 (April): 668–676. http://dx.doi.org/10.1016/j.biopsych.2014.08.013.

McGonigal, Kelly. 2015. *The Upside of Stress: Why Stress Is Good For You, and How To Get Good At It.* New York: Avery.

Szalavitz, Maia. 2011. "The Goldilocks Principle of Stress: Too Little is Almost as Bad as Too Much." *Time,* December 20, 2011. https://healthland.time.com/2011/12/20/the-goldilocks-principle-of-stress-too-little-is-almost-as-bad-as-too-much/?.

Taylor, Shelley. E., Laura Cousio Klein, Brian P. Gruenewald, Tara L. Gurung, Regan Gurung, and John A. Updegraff. 2000. "Biobehavioral responses to stress in females: Tend-and-Befriend, not fight-or-flight." *Psychological Review* 107, no. 3 (July): 411–429. https://doi.org/10.1037/0033-295x.107.3.411.

Taylor, Shelley E. 2006. "Tend and Befriend: Behavioral Bases of Affiliation Under Stress." *Current Directions in Psychological Science* 15, no. 6 (December): 273–277. http://dx.doi.org/10.1111/j.1467-8721.2006.00451.x.

The Fork in the Road

Crum, Alia J., Peter Salovey, and Shawn Achor. 2013. "Rethinking stress: The role of mindsets in determining the stress response." *Journal of Personality and Social Psychology* 104, no. 4: 716–733. https://doi.org/10.1037/a0031201.

Dhabhar, Firdaus S. 2009. "Enhancing versus Suppressive Effects of Stress on Immune Function: Implications for Immunoprotection and Immunopathology." *NeuroImmunoModulation* 16, no. 5 (June): 300–17. https://doi.org/10.1159/000216188.

Huberman, Andrew. 2022. "Dr. Alia Crum: Science of Mindsets for Health & Performance." *Huberman Lab Podcast.* Released January 24, 2022. 1 hr. 37 min. https://hubermanlab.com/dr-alia-crum-science-of-mindsets-for-health-performance/.

Maté, Gabor, and Daniel Maté. 2022. *The Myth of Normal: Trauma, Illness & Healing in a Toxic World*. New York: Avery.

McEwen, Bruce. 1998. "Protective and Damaging Effects of Stress Mediators." *New England Journal of Medicine* 338, no. 3: 171–79. https://doi.org/10.31887/dcns.2006.8.4/bmcewen.

McEwen, Bruce. 2005. "Stressed or stressed out: What is the difference?" *Journal of Psychiatry Neuroscience* 30, no. 5: 315–18. http://www.ncbi.nlm.nih.gov/pmc/articles/pmc1197275/.

Sorrells, Shawn F., Javiar R. Caso, Javier, Carolina D. Munhoz, and Robert M. Sapolski. 2009. "The Stressed CNS: When Glucocorticoids Aggravate Inflammation." *Neuron* 64, no. 1 (October): 33–9. https://doi.org/10.1016%2Fj.neuron.2009.09.032.

Stressism

Purser, Ronald. 2019a. "McMindfulness and The Mantra of Stress." *Mindful Leader (blog)*. July 9, 2019. https://www.mindfulleader.org/blog/27496-mcmindfulness-and-the-mantra-of-stress.

Purser, Ronald. 2019b. "The Mindfulness Conspiracy." *Guardian,* June 14, 2019. https://www.theguardian.com/lifeandstyle/2019/jun/14/the-mindfulness-conspiracy-capitalist-spirituality.

Richards, Shola. 2017. *Making Work Work: The Solution for Bringing Positive Change to Any Work Environment*. Read by Shola Richards. Landover, MD: Gildan Media. Audible audio ed., 7 hr., 12 min.

Richards, Shola. 2020. "Why I'll Never Walk Alone." *Shola Richards Blog (blog)*, LinkedIn. May 30, 2020. https://www.linkedin.com/pulse/why-ill-never-walk-alone-shola-richards/.

Ungar, Michael. 2018. *Change Your World: The Science of Resilience and the True Path to Success*. Toronto, Ontario: Sutherland House.

Sometime Calm IS the Goal

Denby, David. 2016. "The Limits of 'Grit.'" *New Yorker*, June 2016. https://www.newyorker.com/culture/culture-desk/the-limits-of-grit.

Hughes, Karen, Mark A Bellis, Katherine A Hardcastle, Dinesh Sethi, Alexander Butchart, Christopher Mikton, Lisa Jones, and Michael P Dunne. 2017. "The effect of multiple adverse childhood experiences on health: a systematic review and meta-analysis." *Lancet Public Health* 8, no. 2 (August): e356–e366. https://doi.org/10.1016/s2468-2667(17)30118-4.

Maté, Gabor, and Daniel Maté. 2022. *The Myth of Normal: Trauma, Illness & Healing in a Toxic World*. New York: Avery.

Osborne, Karen. 2022. "The Inaugural Episode." *Living In the Sandwich Zone*. Released on January 12, 2022. 12 min. https://podcasters.spotify.com/pod/show/karen-osborne9/episodes/Living-In-the-Sandwich-Zone-The-Inaugural-Episode-e1cpv8r.

Santino, Will (@WillSantinoIllustration). 2023. "When Life Gives You Lemons." Facebook, February 7, 2023.

Seltzer, Leon F. 2022. "You Don't Choose Your Defenses, Your Defenses Choose You." *Psychology Today Blog* (blog), *Psychology Today.* September 22, 2022. https://www.psychologytoday.com/us/blog/evolution-the-self/202209/you-don-t-choose-your-defenses-your-defenses-choose-you.

Yehuda, Rachel, Stephanie Mulherin Engel, Sarah R Brand, Jonathan Seckl, Sue M Marcus, and Gertrud S Berkowitz. 2005.

"Transgenerational Effects of Posttraumatic Stress Disorder in Babies of Mothers Exposed to the World Trade Center Attacks during Pregnancy." *The Journal of Clinical Endocrinology & Metabolism* 90, no. 7 (July): 4115–18. https://doi.org/10.1210/jc.2005-0550.

Yehuda, Rachel, Nikolaos P Daskalakis, Linda M Bierer, Heather N Bader, Torsten Klengel, Florian Holsboer, and Elisabeth B Binder. 2016. "Holocaust exposure induced intergenerational effects on FKBP5 methylation." *Biological Psychiatry* 80, no. 5: 372–80. https://doi.org/10.1016/j.biopsych.2015.08.005.

Yehuda, Rachel. 2022. "How Parents' Trauma Leaves Biological Traces in Children." *Scientific American*, July 2022. https://www.scientificamerican.com/article/how-parents-rsquo-trauma-leaves-biological-traces-in-children/.

Wolynn, Mark. 2016. *It Didn't Start With You: How Inherited Family Trauma Shapes Who We Are and How to End The Cycle.* New York: Penguin Books.

Soul Speak

Chen, Wen G, Dana Shloesser, Angela M Arensdorf, Janine M Simmons, Changhai Cui, Rita Valentino, James W Gnadt, Lisbeth Nielsen, Coryse St. Hillaire-Clarke, Victoria Spruance, Todd S Horowitz, Yolanda F Vallejo, and Helene M Langevin. 2021. "The Emerging Science of Interoception: Sensing, Integrating, Interpreting, and Regulating Signals with the Self." *Trends in Neurosciences* 44, no. 1 (January): 3–16. https://doi.org/10.1016/j.tins.2020.10.007.

Fehmi, Les, and Jim Robbins. 2007. *The Open-Focus Brain: Harnessing the Power of Attention to Heal Mind and Body*. Boulder, CO: Trumpeter.

Fisher, Dana, Matthias Messner, and Olga Pollatos. 2017. "Improvement of Interoceptive Processes after an 8-week

Body Scan Intervention." *Frontiers in Human Neuroscience* 11, (Sept 12): 452. https://doi.org/10.3389/fnhum.2017.00452.

Fukushima, Hirokata, Yuri Terasawa, and Satoshi Umeda. 2010. "Association between interoception and empathy: Evidence from Heartbeat - evoked brain potential." *International Journal of Psychophysiology* 79, no. 2 (February): 259–265. https://doi.org/10.1016/j.ijpsycho.2010.10.015.

Garfinkel, Sarah N., Anil K. Seth, Adam B. Barrett, Keisuke Suzuki, and Hugo D. Critchley. 2015. "Knowing your own heart: Distinguishing interoceptive accuracy from interoceptive awareness." *Biological Psychology* 104 (January): 65–74. https://doi.org/10.1016/j.biopsycho.2014.11.004.

Gibson, Jonathan. 2019. "Mindfulness, Interoception, and the Body: A Contemporary Perspective." *Frontiers in Psychology* 10 (September): 1–18. https://doi.org/10.3389/fpsyg.2019.02012.

Haase, Lori, Jennifer L. Stewart, Brittany Youssef, April C. May, Sara Isakovic, Alan N. Simmons, Douglas C. Johnson, Eric G. Potterat, and Martin P. Paulus. 2016. "When the brain does not adequately feel the body: Links between low resilience and interoception." *Biological Psychology* 113, (January): 37–45. https://doi.org/10.1016/j.biopsycho.2015.11.004.

Juhan, Deane. 1987. *Job's Body: A Handbook for Bodywork.* New York: Station Hill Press.

Mayo Clinic Staff. 2023. "Dissociative Disorders: Diagnosis & Treatment." Mayo Clinic. Accessed March 13, 2023. https://www.mayoclinic.org/diseases-conditions/dissociative-disorders/diagnosis-treatment/drc-20355221.

Myers, Thomas. 2018. "What Am I Feeling? Recent Research on Interoceptive Sensors of the Myofascia." *Massage Magazine (blog)*. December 18, 2018. https://www.massagemag.com/interoceptive-sensors-of-the-myofascia-109064/.

Paul, Annie Murphy. 2021. *The Extended Mind: The Power of Thinking Outside the Brain.* Boston: Houghton Mifflin Harcourt.

Paulus, Martin P., Eric G. Potterat, Marcus K. Taylor, Karl F. Van Orden, James Bauman, Naushee Momen, Genieleah A. Padilla, and Judith L. Swain. 2009. "A neuroscience approach to optimizing brain resources for human performance in extreme environments." *Biobehavioral Reviews* 33, no. 7 (July): 1080–1088. https://doi.org/10.1016/j.neubiorev.2009.05.003.

Plans, David. 2019. "We've Lost Touch With Our Bodies: But We Can Get It Back With Through a Process Known As 'Interoception.'" *Scientific American*, February 2019. https://blogs.scientificamerican.com/observations/weve-lost-touch-with-our-bodies/.

Price, Cynthia. 2016. "Interoceptive Awareness Helps Your Clients Help Themselves." *Massage Magazine (blog).* Oct 1, 2016. https://www.massagemag.com/interoceptive-awareness-helps-your-clients-help-themselves.

Price, Cynthia J., Elaine Adams Thompson, Sheila Crowell, and Kenneth Pike. 2019. "Longitudinal effects of interoceptive awareness training through mindful awareness in body-oriented therapy (MABT) as an adjunct to women's substance use disorder treatment: A randomized controlled trial." *Drug and Alcohol Dependence* 198 (May): 140–149. https://doi.org/10.1016/j.drugalcdep.2019.02.012.

Quadt, Lisa, Sarah N. Garfinkel, James S. Mulcahy, Dennis E.O. Larsson, Marta Silva, Anna-Marie Jones, Clara Strauss, and Hugo D. Critchley. "Interoceptive training to target anxiety in autistic adults (ADIE): A single-center, superiority randomized controlled trial." *EClinicalMedicine* 39, no. 101042 (July). https://doi.org/10.1016/j.eclinm.2021.101042.

Robson, David. 2021. "Interoception: the hidden sense that shapes wellbeing." *Guardian*, August 15, 2021.

https://www.theguardian.com/science/2021/aug/15/the-hidden-sense-shaping-your-wellbeing-interoception.

Seabury, Tom, David Benton, and Hayley A. Young. 2023. "Interoceptive differences in elite sprint and long-distance runners: A multidimensional investigation." *PLoS ONE* 18, no. 1 (January): e0278067. https://doi.org/10.1371/journal.pone.0278067.

Van Der Kolk, Bessel. 2014. *The Body Keeps the Score: Brain, Mind, and Body in The Healing of Trauma.* New York: Penguin Books.

It's Complicated

Barrett, Lisa Feldman. 2017. *How Emotions Are Made: The Secret Life of the Brain.* New York: Houghton Mifflin Harcourt.

Damasio, Antonio. 2021. *Feeling & Knowing: Making Minds Conscious.* New York: Pantheon Books.

Porges, Stephen W. 2021. "Polyvagal Theory: A biobehavioral journey to sociality." *Comprehensive Psychoneuroendocrinology* 7, no. 100069 (August): 1–7. https://doi.org/10.1016/j.cpnec.2021.100069.

Van der Kolk, Bessel. 2014. *The Body Keeps the Score: Brain, Mind, and Body in The Healing of Trauma.* New York: Penguin Books.

The Stillness Seesaw

APA Dictionary of Psychology. *APA Dictionary of Psychology.* 2nd edition. Washington DC: American Psychological Association. https://dictionary.apa.org/burnout.

Benazzo, Maurizio, and Zaya Benazzo, directors. 2021. *The Wisdom of Trauma: A Journey to the root of human pain and the source of healing with Dr. Gabor Maté. Science and Nonduality.* 1 hr, 27 m.

Brown, Brené. 2021. *Atlas of the Heart: Mapping Meaningful Connection and the Language of Human Experience.* New York: Penguin Random House.

Johnson, Kimberly Ann. 2021. *Call of the Wild: How We Heal Trauma, Awaken Our Own Power, and Use It For Good.* New York: Harper Wave.

Maté, Gabor, and Daniel Maté. 2022. *The Myth of Normal: Trauma, Illness & Healing in a Toxic World.* New York: Avery.

Porges, Stephen. 2020. *Foundational Safe and Sound Protocol (SSP) Training & Certification.* Unyte and iLs Listening Systems. Accessed May 5, 2023. https://integratedlistening.com/products/ssp-safe-sound-protocol/certification/.

Chronic Pain

Abdallah, Chadi G., and Paul Geha. 2017. "Chronic Pain and Chronic Stress: Two Sides of the Same Coin." *Chronic Stress* 1 (February). https://doi.org/10.1177/2470547017704763.

Apkarian, Vania. 2020. "Dr. Vania Apkarian: Chronic Low Back Pain - Should Treatment Focus on Back or Brain?" Aivo Health. June 17, 2020. 3:53. https://www.youtube.com/watch?v=RuEo7SRINUs.

Elliot, James, Timothy Flynn, Aiman Al-Najjar, Joel Press, Bao Nguyen, and Jon Timothy Noteboom. 2011. "The Pearls and Pitfalls of Magnetic Resonance Imaging for the Spine." *Journal of Orthopaedic & Sports Physical Therapy* 41, no. 11 (November): 803–905. https://doi.org/10.2519/jospt.2011.3636.

Gordon, Alan, and Alon Ziv. 2021. *The Way Out: A Revolutionary, Scientifically Proven Approach to Healing Chronic Pain.* New York: Avery.

Hannibal, Kara E., and Mark D. Bishop. 2014. "Chronic Stress, Cortisol Dysfunction, and Pain: A Psychoneuroendocrine Rationale for Stress Management in Pain Rehabilitation."

Physical Therapy 94, no. 12 (December): 1816–1825. https://doi.org/10.2522/ptj.20130597.

Mansour, Ali R., Marwan Baliki, Leijan Huang, Souraya Torbey, Kristi M. Herrmann, Thomas J. Schnitzer, and Vania A. Apkarian. 2013. "Brain white matter structural properties predict transition to chronic pain." *Pain* 154, no. 10 (October): 2160–68. https://doi.org/10.1016/j.pain.2013.06.044.

Moseley, Lorimer G., and David S. Butler. 2017. *Explain Pain Supercharged: The Clinician's Manual.* South Australia: Noigroup Publications.

Before We Begin

Dana, Deb. 2020. *Polyvagal Exercises for Safety and Connection: 50 Client-Centered Practices.* New York: W.W. Norton & Company.

Levine, Peter, and Ann Fredrick. 1997. *Waking the Tiger: Healing Trauma.* Berkeley, California: North Atlantic Books.

Breathe

Balban, Melis Yilmaz, Eric Neri, Manuela M. Kogon, Jamie M. Zeitzer, David Spiegel, and Andrew D. Huberman. 2023. "Brief structured respiration practices enhance mood and reduce physiological arousal." *Cell Reports Medicine* 4, no. 1 (January). https://doi.org/10.1016/j.xcrm.2022.100895.

Blackburn, Elizabeth, and Elissa Epel. 2017. *The Telomere Effect.* New York: Grand Central Publishing.

Blasco-Lafarga, Cristina, Cristina García-Soriano, and Pablo Monteagudo. 2020. "Autonomic Modulation Improves in Response to Harder Performances While Playing Wind Instruments." *Archives of Neuroscience* 7, no. 2 (April): e101969. https://doi.org/10.5812/ans.101969.

Bond, Mary. 2007. *The New Rules of Posture: How to Sit, Stand, and Move in the Modern World.* Rochester, Vermont: Healing Arts Press.

Huberman, Andrew. 2021. "Tools for Managing Stress & Anxiety." *Huberman Lab Podcast.* Released March 8, 2021. 1 hr., 38 min. https://hubermanlab.com/tools-for-managing-stress-and-anxiety/.

Hyman, Mark. 2022. "The Power of Breath As Medicine with James Nestor." *The Doctor's Farmacy with Mark Hyman M.D.* Released April 6, 2022. 1 hr. 1 min. https://drhyman.com/blog/2022/04/06/podcast-ep520/.

Nestor, James. 2020. *Breath: The New Science of a Lost Art.* New York: Riverhead Books.

Ortego, Gorka, Jorge Hugo Villiafañe, Victor Doménech-García, Pedro Berjano, Lucia Bertozzi, and Pablo Herrero. 2016. "Is there a relationship between psychological stress or anxiety and chronic nonspecific neck-arm pain in adults? A systematic review and meta-analysis." *Journal of Psychosomatic Research* 90 (November): 70–81. https://doi.org/10.1016/j.jpsychores.2016.09.006.

Wapner, Jessica. 2020. "Vision and Breathing May Be the Secrets to Surviving 2020." *Scientific American*, November 2020. https://www.scientificamerican.com/article/vision-and-breathing-may-be-the-secrets-to-surviving-2020/.

Yackle, Kevin, Lindsay A. Schwarz, Kaiwen Kam, Jordan M. Sorokin, John R. Huguenard, Jack L. Feldman, Liguen Luo, and Mark A. Krasnow. 2017. "Breathing control center neurons that promote arousal in mice." *Science* 355, no. 6332 (March): 1411–1415. https://doi.org/10.1126/science.aai7984.

Zaccaro, Andrea, Andrea Piarulli, Marco Laurino, Erika Garbella, Danilo Menicucci, Bruno Neri, and Angelo Gemignani. 2018. "How breath-control can change your life: A systematic review on Psycho-physiological correlates of slow breathing." *Frontiers in Human Neuroscience* 12 (September): 353. https://doi.org/10.3389/fnhum.2018.00353.

Move

Crum, Alia J., and Ellen J. Langer. 2007. "Mind-Set Matters: Exercise and the Placebo Effect." *Science 18*, no. 2 (February): 165–171. https://doi.org/10.1111/j.1467-9280.2007.01867.x.

Drum, Richard P., David J. Levinthal, and Peter L. Strick. 2016. "Motor, Cognitive, and Affective Areas of the Cerebral Cortex Influence the Adrenal Medualla." *Proceedings of the National Academy of Sciences* 113, no. 35 (March): 9922–9927. https://doi.org/10.1073/pnas.1605044113.

Hamblin, James. 2015. "Why One Neuroscientist Started Blasting His Core." *Atlantic, August* 24, 2016. https://www.theatlantic.com/science/archive/2016/08/cortical-adrenal-orchestra/496679/.

Kozlowska, Kasia, Peter Walker, Loyola McLean, and Pascal Carrive. 2015. "Fear and the Defense Cascade: Clinical Implications and Management." *Harvard Review of Psychiatry* 23, no. 4 (July): 263–287. https://doi.org/10.1097/hrp.0000000000000065.

McGonigal, Kelly. 2019. *The Joy of Movement: How Exercise Helps Us Find Happiness, Hope, Connection, and Courage.* New York: Avery.

Pontzer, Herman. 2021. *Burn: How Research Blows the Lid Off How We Really Burn Calories, Lose Weight, and Stay Healthy.* New York: Avery.

Ratey, John J., and Eric Hagerman. 2008. *Spark: The Revolutionary New Science of Exercise and the Brain.* New York: Little Brown Company.

Sinclair, David A., and Matthew D. LaPlente. 2019. *Lifespan: Why We Age - and Why We Don't Have To.* New York: Atria Books.

Todd, Neil, and Christopher Lee. 2015. "The sensory-motor theory of rhythm and beat induction 20 years on: a new synthesis and future perspectives." *Frontiers in Human Neuroscience* 9 (August). http://dx.doi.org/10.3389/fnhum.2015.00444.

Wagner, Heiko, Ulrich Rehmes, Daniel Kohle, and Christian Puta. "Laughing: A Demanding Exercise for Trunk Muscles." *Journal of Motor Behavior* 46, no. 1 (November): 33–7. https://doi.org/10.1080/00222895.2013.844091.

Stretch

Bandy, William D., Jean M. Irion, and Michelle Briggler. 1997. "The Effect of Time and Frequency of Static Stretching on Flexibility of the Hamstring Muscles." *Physical Therapy* 10, no. 1 (October): 1090–1096. https://doi.org/10.1093/ptj/77.10.1090.

Eccles, Jessica. 2017. "What is the link between joint hypermobility and anxiety?" The Academy of Medical Science. October 4, 2017. 4:33. https://www.youtube.com/watch?v=Mjo7rdAv5ps.

Hinsley, Libby. 2022. *Yoga for Bendy People: Optimizing the Benefits of Yoga for Hypermobility.* Potomac, MD: New Degree Press. Kindle.

Koch, Liz. 2012.*The Psoas Book: 30th Anniversary Revised Edition.* Felton, CA: Guineas Pig Publications.

Ortego, Gorka, Jorge Hugo Villiafañe, Victor Doménech-García, Pedro Berjano, Lucia Bertozzi, and Pablo Herrero. 2016. "Is there a relationship between psychological stress or anxiety and chronic nonspecific neck-arm pain in adults? A systematic review and meta-analysis." *Journal of Psychosomatic Research* 90 (November): 70–81. https://doi.org/10.1016/j.jpsychores.2016.09.006.

Schleifer, Lawrence, Thomas Spalding, Scott Kerick, Jeffrey Cram, Ronald Ley, and Bradley Hatfield. 2008. "Mental stress and trapezius muscle activation under psychomotor challenge: A focus on EMG gaps during computer work." *Psychophysiology 45*, no. 3 (February): 356–365. https://doi.org/10.1111/j.1469-8986.2008.00645.x.

Williams, Caroline. 2021. *Move: How the New Science of Body Movement Can Set Your Mind Free.* Toronto: Hanover Square Press.

Wyon, Matthew, Lee Felton, and Shaun Galloway. 2009. "A Comparison of Two Stretching Modalities on Lower-Limb Range of Motion Measurements in Recreational Dancers." *The Journal of Strength and Conditioning Research* 23, no. 7 (October): 2144–2148. https://doi.org/10.1519/jsc.0b013e3181b3e198.

Eat

Babb, Michelle. 2020. *Mastering Mindful Eating: Transform Your Relationship with Food.* Seattle, WA: Sasquatch Books.

Baek, Jinhee, Sukchan Lee, Taesup Cho, Seong-Wook Kim, Minsoo Kim, Yongwoo Yoon, Ko Keun Kim, Junweon Byun, Sang Jeong Kim, Jaeseung Jeong, and Hee-Sup Shin. 2019. "Neural circuits underlying a psychotherapeutic regimen for fear disorders." *Nature* 566, no. 7744 (February): 339–343. https://doi.org/10.1038/s41586-019-0931-y.

Blackburn, Elizabeth, and Elissa Epel. 2017. *The Telomere Effect: A Revolutionary Approach to Living Younger, Healthier, Longer.* New York: Grand Central Publishing.

Chamine, Shirzad. 2012. *Positive Intelligence: Why Only 20% of Teams and Individuals Achieve Their True Potential AND HOW YOU CAN ACHIEVE YOURS.* Austin, TX: Greenleaf Book Group Press.

Delker, Eric, Bander AlYami, Linda Gallo, John Ruiz, Moyses Szklo, and Matthew Allison. 2021. "Chronic Stress Burden, Visceral Adipose Tissue, and Adiposity-Related Inflammation: The Multi-Ethnic Study of Atherosclerosis." *Psychosomatic Medicine* 83, no. 8 (October): 834–842. https://doi.org/10.1097/psy.0000000000000983.

Epel, Elissa, Bruce McEwen, Teresa Seeman, Karen Mattews, Grace Castellazzo, Kelly Brownell, Jennifer Bell, and Jeanette Ickovics. 2000. "Stress and Body Shape: Stress-Induced Cortisol Secretion Is Consistently Greater Among Women with Central Fat." *Psychosomatic Medicine 65,* no. 5 (September): 623–632. https://doi.org/10.1097/00006842-200009000-00005.

Fothergill, Erin, Juen Guo, Lilian Howard, Jennifer Kerns, Nicolas Knuth, Robert Brychta, Kong Y. Chen, Monica Skarulis, Mary Walter, Peter Walter, and Kevin Hall. 2016. "Persistent metabolic adaptation 6 years after 'The Biggest Loser' competition." *Obesity* 24, no. 8 (August): 1612–1619. https://pubmed.ncbi.nlm.nih.gov/27136388/.

Godoy, Maria. 2020. "How Body Positivity Can Lead to Better Health." NPR Life Kit (blog), *NPR*. May 22, 2020. https://www.npr.org/2019/04/25/717058366/rethinking-weight-loss-boost-your-body-acceptance-for-better-health.

Hanlon, Erin, Esra Tasali, Rachel Leproult, Kara Stuhr, Elizabeth Doncheck, Harriet de Wit, Cecilia J. Hillard, and Eve Van Cauter. 2016. "Sleep Restriction Enhances the Daily Rhythm of Circulating Levels of Endocannabinoid 2-Arachidonoylglycerol." *Sleep* 39, no. 3 (March): 653–664. https://doi.org/10.5665/sleep.5546.

Kiecolt-Glaser, Janice, Diane Habash, Christopher Fagundes, Rebecca Andridge, Juan Peng, William Malarkey, and Martha Belury. 2014. "Daily Stressors, Past Depression, and Metabolic Responses to High-Fat Meals: A Novel Path to Obesity."

Biological Psychiatry 77, no. 7 (July): 653–660. https://doi.org/10.1016%2Fj.biopsych.2014.05.018.

Kyrou, Ioannis, and Constantine Tsigos. 2009. "Stress hormones: physiological stress and regulation of metabolism." *Current Opinion in Pharmacology* 9, no. 6 (December): 787–793. https://doi.org/10.1016/j.coph.2009.08.007.

Rosenberg, Stanley. 2017. *Accessing the Healing Power of the Vagus Nerve: Self-Help Exercises for Anxiety, Depression, Trauma, and Autism.* Berkley, CA: North Atlantic Books.

Tribole, Evelyn, and Elyse Resch. 2012. *Intuitive Eating: A Revolutionary Program That Works.* New York: St. Martin's Griffin.

Sense

Johnson, Kimberly Ann. 2021. *Call of the Wild: How We Heal Trauma, Awaken Our Own Power, and Use It for Good.* New York: Harper Wave.

Wapner, Jessica. 2020. "Vision and Breathing May Be the Secrets to Surviving 2020." *Scientific American*, November 2020. https://www.scientificamerican.com/article/vision-and-breathing-may-be-the-secrets-to-surviving-2020.

Our Connection to Connections

Birdsong, Mia. 2020. *How We Show Up: Reclaiming Family, Friendship, and Community.* Read by Mia Birdsong. New York: Hachette Go. Audible audio ed., 6 hr., 46 min.

Dana, Deb. 2020. *Polyvagal Exercises for Safety and Connection: 50 Client-Centered Practices*. New York: W.W. Norton & Company.

Gibson, Lindsay C. 2020. *Who You Were Meant to Be: A Guide to Finding or Recovering Your Life's Purpose.* Second edition. Virginia Beach, VA: Blue Bird Press.

Lamott, Anne. 2022. Facebook, April 5, 2022. https://www.facebook.com/AnneLamott/posts/524381439050367/.

Leland, John. 2022. "How Loneliness Is Damaging Our Health." *New York Times,* April 20, 2022. https://www.nytimes.com/2022/04/20/nyregion/loneliness-epidemic.html.

Nagoski, Emily, and Amelia Nagoski. 2019. *Burnout: The Secret to Unlocking the Stress Cycle.* New York: Ballantine Books.

Perry, Bruce C., and Oprah Winfrey. 2021. *What Happened to You? Conversations on Trauma, Resilience, and Healing.* New York: Flatiron Books.

Pinker, Susan. 2017. "The Secret to Living Longer May Be Your Social Life." Released August 18, 2017. TED Talk, 15:53. https://www.ted.com/talks/susan_pinker_the_secret_to_living_longer_may_be_your_social_life.

Porges, Stephen W. 2017. *The Pocket Guide to the Polyvagal Theory: The Transformative Power of Feeling Safe.* New York: W.W. Norton & Company.

Tarraf, Laila. 2021. *Strong Like Water: How I Found the Courage to Lead with Love in Business and in Life.* Read by Laila Tarraf. Berkley, California: She Writes Press. Audible audio ed., 6 hr., 39 min.

Thomashauer, Regena. 2016. *Pussy: A Reclamation*. Carlsbad, California: Hay House, Inc.

Broken Connections

Brown, Brené. 2021. *Atlas of the Heart: Mapping Meaningful Connection and the Language of Human Experience.* New York: Penguin Random House.

Dana, Deb. 2020. *Polyvagal Exercises for Safety and Connection: 50 Client-Centered Practices.* New York: W.W. Norton & Company.

Eisenberg, Naomi. 2015. "Social Pain and the Brain: Controversies, Questions, and Where to Go from Here." *Annual Review of Psychology* 66, no. 1 (January): 601–629. https://doi.org/10.1146/annurev-psych-010213-115146.

Menekem, Resmaa. 2017. *My Grandmother's Hands: Racialized Trauma and the Pathway to Mending Our Hearts and Bodies.* Las Vegas, NV: Central Recovery Press.

Thích Nhất Hạnh. 2023. "Quotes." *Thich Nhat Hanh Foundation.* January 22, 2023. https://thichnhathanhfoundation.org/covid-resources-quotes.

Parenting

Ghati, Nirmal, Avantika K. Killa, Gautam Sharma, Biju Karunakaran, Aman Agarwal, Sriloy Mohanty, L. Nivethitha, Deepti Siddharthan, and R. M. Pandey. 2021. "A randomized trial of the immediate effect of Bee-Humming Breathing exercise on blood pressure and heart rate variability in patients with essential hypertension." *Explore* 17, no. 4 (July-August): 312–319. https://doi.org/10.1016/j.explore.2020.03.009.

Grape, Christina, Maria Sandgren, Lars-Olof Hansson, Mats Ericson, and Töres Theorell. 2002. "Does singing promote well-being?: An empirical study of professional and amateur singers during a singing lesson." *Integrative Physiological & Behavioral Science* 38, no. 1: 65–75. https://doi.org/10.1007/bf02734261.

Perlman, Susan B., Linda A. Camras, and Kevin A. Pelphrey. 2008. "Physiology and functioning: Parents' vagal tone, emotion socialization, and children's emotion knowledge." *Journal of Experimental Child Psychology* 100, no. 4 (August): 308–315. https://doi.org/10.1016/j.jecp.2008.03.007.

Porges, Stephen W. 2021. "Polyvagal Theory: A biobehavioral journey to sociality." *Comprehensive*

Psychoneuroendocrinology 7, no. 100069 (August): 1–7. https://doi.org/10.1016/j.cpnec.2021.100069.

Improving Relationships

Chapman, Gary. 2015. *The 5 Love Languages: The Secret to Love That Lasts.* Chicago, Illinois: Northfield Publishing.

Doyle, Glennon. 2020. *Untamed.* New York: The Dial Press.

Kozlowska, Kasia, Peter Walker, Loyola McLean, and Pascal Carrive. 2015. "Fear and the Defense Cascade: Clinical Implications and Management." *Harvard Review of Psychiatry* 23, no. 4 (July): 263–287.https://doi.org/10.1097/hrp.0000000000000065.

The Art of Rushing

Burkeman, Oliver. 2021. *Four Thousand Weeks: Time Management for Mortals.* New York: Farrar, Straus, and Giroux.

Glei, Jocelyn K. 2022. "Confessions of a Burnt Out Over-Achiever." *jkglei.com*. Accessed April 2, 2022. https://jkglei.com/burnout/.

Headlee, Celeste. 2020. *Do Nothing: How to Break Away from Overworking, Overdoing, and Underliving.* New York: Harmony Books.

Kukla, Elliot. 2022. "The Most Valuable Thing I Can Teach My Kid Is How to Be Lazy." *New York Times*, January 20, 2022. https://www.nytimes.com/2022/01/20/opinion/teach-children-to-be-lazy.html.

Pushing into Uncomfortable

Brooks, Arthur C. 2022. *From Strength to Strength: Finding Success, Happiness, and Deep Purpose in the Second Half of Life.* New York: Portfolio/Penguin.

Dana, Deborah. 2020. *Befriending Your Nervous System: Looking Through the Lens of Polyvagal Theory.* Read by Deborah Dana. Louisville, CO: Sounds True Publishing. 8 hr., 24 min.

Gibson, Lindsay. 2023. "Who You Are Meant to Be at Midlife." HappyWomenDinners.com. Streamed live January 2023. Virtual workshop.

Lieberman, Daniel Z., and Michael E. Long. 2018. *The Molecule of More: How a Single Chemical in Your Brain Drives Love, Sex, and Creativity - and Will Determine the Fate of the Human Race.* Dallas, TX: BenBella Books, Inc.

Monroe, Justin, director. 2021. *Holy Frit.* Tandem Arts. 1:59:20.

Cartwheeling into Uncomfortable

Brown, Stuart. 2015. "The opposite of play is not work — it is depression." *News & Events* (blog), Wu Tsai Neurosciences Institute, Stanford University. May 29, 2015. https://neuroscience.stanford.edu/news/opposite-play-not-work-it-depression.

Cameron, Julia. 2016. *The Artist's Way: A Spiritual Path to Higher Creativity.* New York: TarcherPerigee.

Hoehn, Charlie. 2014. *Play It Away: A Workaholic's Cure for Anxiety.* CO: CharlieHoehn.com.

Huberman, Andrew. 2022. "Dr. Alia Crum: Science of Mindsets for Health & Performance." *Huberman Lab Podcast.* Released January 24, 2022. 1 hr. 37 min. https://hubermanlab.com/dr-alia-crum-science-of-mindsets-for-health-performance/.

Keltner, Dacher. 2023. *Awe: The New Science of Everyday Wonder and How It Can Transform Your Life.* New York: Penguin Press.

Miller, Lisa. 2021. *The Awakened Brain: The New Science of Spirituality and Our Quest for An Inspired Life.* New York: Penguin Random House.

Santos, Laurie. 2022. "Fighting that 'Meh' Feeling of Languishing." *The Happiness Lab.* Released

February 13, 2022. 41 mins., 53 seconds. https://www.pushkin.fm/podcasts/the-happiness-lab-with-dr-laurie-santos/fighting-that-meh-feeling-of-languishing.

Siviy, Stephen M., and Jaak Panksepp. 2011. "In search of the neurobiological substrates for social playfulness in mammalian brains." *Neuroscience & Behavioral Reviews* 35, no. 9 (October): 1821–1830. https://doi.org/10.1016/j.neubiorev.2011.03.006.

Final(ly) Thoughts

Campbell, Joseph. 2018. *A Joseph Campbell Companion: Reflections on the Art of Living.* Read by Braden Wright, Tom Parks, and David deVries. Grand Haven, Michigan: Brilliance Audio. Audible audio ed., 8 hr., 51 min.

Schwartz, Richard C. 2021. *No Bad Parts: Healing Trauma and Restoring Wholeness with The Internal Family Systems Model.* Boulder, CO: Sounds True.

Photo by Danny Brown, 2023

About the Author

Chantal Donnelly is a physical therapist, Resilience Toolkit facilitator, and founder of the wellness company Body Insight Inc. She holds degrees in psychology and kinesiology from Occidental College and a master's in physical therapy from Mount Saint Mary's College in Los Angeles.

Chantal is certified in Pilates, a practitioner of Safe and Sound Protocol, and writer, producer, and star of the exercise and rehabilitation videos *Strong Knees* and *Pain-Free* at Work.

She currently practices physical therapy, Pilates-based rehabilitation, and stress management at her private clinic in Pasadena, California.

She is best known as "Ed's wife" and "Aidan's mom" and wouldn't have it any other way.

Chantal invites you to follow her on Instagram @ BodyInsightInc and on Facebook at https://www.facebook.com/BodyInsightInc.

You can visit her website at https://www.bodyinsight.com/.